Three nine across

Published by
The Bible Reading Fellowship
15 The Chambers, Vineyard
Abingdon OX14 3FE
United Kingdom
Tel: +44 (0)1865 319700
Email: enquiries@brf.org.uk
Website: www.brf.org.uk

ISBN 978 1 84101 547 7
First published 2008
Reprinted 2008, 2009
10 9 8 7 6 5 4 3 2

Acknowledgments
Unless otherwise stated, scripture quotations are taken from the Holy Bible, New International Version, copyright © 1973, 1978, 1984 by International Bible Society, and are used by permission of Hodder & Stoughton Publishers, a division of Hodder Headline Ltd. All rights reserved. 'NIV' is a registered trademark of International Bible Society. UK trademark number 1448790.

A catalogue record for this book is available from the British Library

Printed in the UK by CPI Bookmarque, Croydon, CR0 4TD

Three down nine across

80 Bible-based crosswords

John Capon

Introduction

In one sense, a book of crossword puzzles is something of a contradiction in terms. A crossword, after all, is usually just one small item in a newspaper or magazine—something to be done as part of the process of relating to the whole of the contents, like the weather forecast or the share prices. A book containing only page after page of crosswords would seem to be an unlikely concept, were it not for the fact that such books appear to be very popular.

What marks this one out as different from most of the rest, however, is that nearly all the answers come from the Bible (The New International Version, first edition). These particular puzzles first appeared in the weekly denominational newspaper *The Baptist Times* and I am grateful to its editor, the Revd Mark Woods, for suggesting the book in the first place. The puzzles have been amended where necessary to make them appropriate to a wider audience. The clues are either alternative words, descriptions, tests of biblical knowledge or missing words from familiar or self-evident Bible texts. Bible references are given, but for the majority of clues they are intended to be used only as a last resort. The small number of non-biblical answers require a modest religious or general knowledge—and each puzzle includes a couple of anagrams to add variety.

Compiling these crosswords (a task I took up only upon retirement as editor of *The Baptist Times*) has increased my biblical knowledge, and I hope the same may be true for those who use this book. Turning up a previously unfamiliar text has often led me to read its context, with consequent benefit. I have made some surprising discoveries, too, such as the existence in the Bible (or at least the NIV) of the word 'terrorists' (see Puzzle No 34).

I hope these puzzles will provide you, the reader of this book, with some not-too-demanding mental activity, and if it sends you back to your Bible into the bargain, well, that can't be bad!

I would like to express my gratitude to all the members of the BRF team and especially my editor, Naomi Starkey, for her encouragement and patience, and to my wife Sue for her forbearance during a long period when she became a 'crossword widow'.

No 1

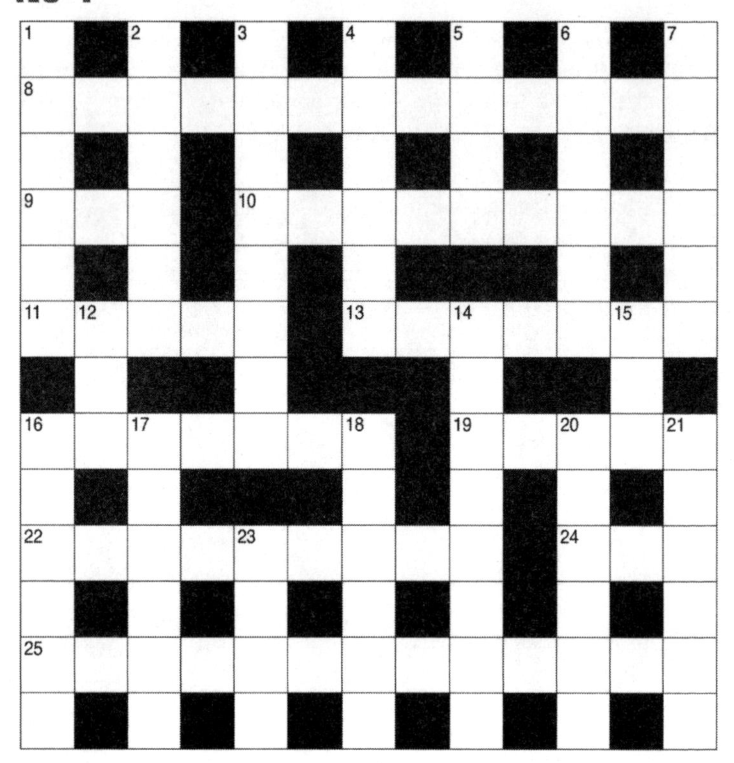

Across

8 'Then Aaron and his sons and — — will be consecrated' *(Exodus 29:21)* (5,8)

9 'He lifted me out of the slimy — , out of the mud and mire' *(Psalm 40:2)* (3)

10 Such a person should be put to death *(Leviticus 20:27)* (9)

11 Chain of mountains *(Numbers 27:12)* (5)

13 'They are worse off at the — — they were at the beginning' *(2 Peter 2:20)* (3,4)

16 Descent (anag.) (7)

19 'But they all alike — to make excuses' *(Luke 14:18)* (5)

22 Reimbursement *(Luke 6:34)* (9)

24 Female sheep *(2 Samuel 12:4)* (3)

25 ‘— — is too wonderful for me, too lofty for me to attain’ *(Psalm 139:6)* (4,9)

Down

1 Alcohol-induced oblivion *(Psalm 78:65)* (6)

2 ‘Three times I was — with rods’ *(2 Corinthians 11:25)* (6)

3 Future outlook *(Proverbs 10:28)* (8)

4 It caused Joseph’s brothers to journey to Egypt to buy grain *(Genesis 42:5)* (6)

5 See 15 Down

6 ‘You care for the land and water it; you — it abundantly’ *(Psalm 65:9)* (6)

7 Son of Mehir and descendant of Judah *(1 Chronicles 4:11)* (6)

12 Car (anag.) (3)

14 Engage in warfare *(Isaiah 31:4)* (2,6)

15 ‘In the thirty-first year of — king of Judah, — became king of Israel’ *(1 Kings 16:23)* (3,4)

16 Excessive strain or tension *(Jeremiah 19:9)* (6)

17 ‘The Son of Man will come at an hour when you do not — him’ *(Luke 12:40)* (6)

18 ‘Very rarely will anyone — — a righteous man’ *(Romans 5:7)* (3,3)

20 Avaricious *(1 Peter 5:2)* (6)

21 ‘Martha, Martha, you are worried and upset about many things, but only one thing is — ’ *(Luke 10:41–42)* (6)

23 ‘For my — is easy and my burden is light’ *(Matthew 11:30)* (4)

No 2

Across

1 Under these Hagar put Ishmael to die *(Genesis 21:15)* (6)

4 Vantage point from which Moses saw the promised land before he died *(Deuteronomy 34:1)* (6)

7 'The Lord is compassionate and gracious, — to anger, abounding in love' *(Psalm 103:8)* (4)

8 'When he sees the wolf coming the hired hand — the sheep and runs away' *(John 10:12)* (8)

9 The world's first steam-worked public railway, — to Darlington (8)

13 It helped to provide the honey inside the carcass of the lion Samson killed *(Judges 14:8)* (3)

16 High Church (5-8)

17 Possessive pronoun (3)

19 Plotting *(Nehemiah 6:2)* (8)
24 'Lovers of — rather than lovers of God' *(2 Timothy 3:4)* (8)
25 Destroy by fire *(Deuteronomy 7:5)* (4)
26 'He who has been stealing must steal no longer, but must work, doing something — with his hands' *(Ephesians 4:28)* (6)
27 One of the colours of the riders' breastplates in John's vision *(Revelation 9:17)* (6)

Down

1 'The father said to his servants, "Quick! Bring me the — robe and put it on him"' *(Luke 15:22)* (4)
2 Ghosts are (anag.) (9)
3 A small one can set a great forest on fire *(James 3:5)* (5)
4 Instrument used as accompaniment in some churches (5)
5 'A Levite, when he came to the place and saw him, passed by on the other — ' *(Luke 10:32)* (4)
6 Swiss illustrator of the Good News Bible, — Vallotton (5)
10 'In the — of Christ I glory, towering o'er the wrecks of time' (5)
11 Paul told Timothy that an overseer in the church must be able to do this *(1 Timothy 3:2)* (5)
12 Comes between Micah and Habakkuk (5)
13 Ill in a bug (anag.) (9)
14 'They saw what seemed to be tongues of fire that separated and came to rest on — of them' *(Acts 2:3)* (4)
15 Controversial artist best-known for his *Christ of St John of the Cross*, Salvador — (4)
18 'Have nothing to do with godless myths and old wives' — ' *(1 Timothy 4:7)* (5)
20 Barbaric *(Jeremiah 6:23)* (5)
21 Adversary *(Luke 10:19)* (5)
22 The portion of his possessions that Zacchaeus told Jesus he would give to the poor *(Luke 19:8)* (4)
23 'Though your sins are like scarlet, they shall be as white as — ' *(Isaiah 1:18)* (4)

No 3

Across

1 'This is a hard teaching. Who can — it?' *(John 6:60)* (6)

4 'As a bride — herself with her jewels' *(Isaiah 61:10)* (6)

8 'Bless those who — you, pray for those who ill-treat you' *(Luke 6:28)* (5)

9 'He was a — man, with a thorough knowledge of the Scriptures' *(Acts 18:24)* (7)

10 Not properly aligned (3,4)

11 Lo, Ben (anag.) (5)

12 'All the — of the Egyptians died' *(Exodus 9:6)* (9)

17 Advantage *(Daniel 11:27)* (5)

19 'That — serpent called the devil' *(Revelation 12:9)* (7)

21 'The — took the men into Joseph's house' *(Genesis 43:24)* (7)

22 I bade (anag.) (5)
23 'And the — with his sickle at harvest' *(Jeremiah 50:16)* (6)
24 'Remember the — from which you have fallen!' *(Revelation 2:5)* (6)

Down

1 Used to secure a ship at sea *(Acts 27:13)* (6)
2 'Be very — , then, how you live' *(Ephesians 5:15)* (7)
3 Portion *(Luke 24:42)* (5)
5 'Let not my heart be — — what is evil' *(Psalm 141:4)* (5,2)
6 Rhythm and Blues (1,3,1)
7 'He said to his sons, " — the donkey for me"' *(1 Kings 13:13)* (6)
9 Source of illumination *(Daniel 5:5)* (9)
13 'Two of them were going to a — called Emmaus' *(Luke 24:13)* (7)
14 'Remember the Sabbath day by — it holy' *(Exodus 20:8)* (7)
15 Roman Emperor *(John 19:15)* (6)
16 'Go to the house of Judas on Straight — ' *(Acts 9:11)* (6)
18 Stadium *(1 Corinthians 4:9)* (5)
20 'Day and night will never — ' *(Genesis 8:22)* (5)

No 4

Across

1 Primatial city of the Church of England's northern province (4)

3 Speaking under oath *(Jeremiah 5:2)* (8)

9 Fallen angel from Milton's *Paradise Lost* (7)

10 'Do not take a — or bag or sandals; and do not greet anyone on the road' *(Luke 10:4)* (5)

11 Abram's father *(Genesis 11:26)* (5)

12 Complied with *(John 17:6)* (6)

14 'My message and my preaching were not with wise and persuasive words, but with a — of the Spirit's power' *(1 Corinthians 2:4)* (13)

17 i.e. palm (anag.) (6)

19 'We always — God for all of you' *(1 Thessalonians 1:2)* (5)

22 Syncretistic religion originating in 19th-century Persia (5)

23 Pariah *(Jeremiah 30:17)* (7)
24 Deter *(Ezekiel 33:8)* (8)
25 'Although I am — than the least of all God's people' *(Ephesians 3:8)* (4)

Down

1 Pagan name for Christmas (8)
2 Happen again (5)
4 How Ezekiel invariably described God speaking, most memorably in the Valley of Dry Bones *(Ezekiel 37:4)* (4,2,3,4)
5 More than sufficient (5)
6 Native of, say, Tel Aviv (7)
7 Great merriment *(Psalm 35:15)* (4)
8 Sheepskin coat (6)
13 Inhabitants of Canaan who struck fear into the Israelites because of their height and strength *(Deuteronomy 1:28)* (8)
15 Ancient city on the Nile for which Jeremiah prophesied doom *(Jeremiah 46:19)* (7)
16 Use tat (anag.) (6)
18 Farewell using all but one vowel (5)
20 Gemstone *(Exodus 28:19)* (5)
21 David's grandfather *(1 Chronicles 2:12–15)* (4)

No 5

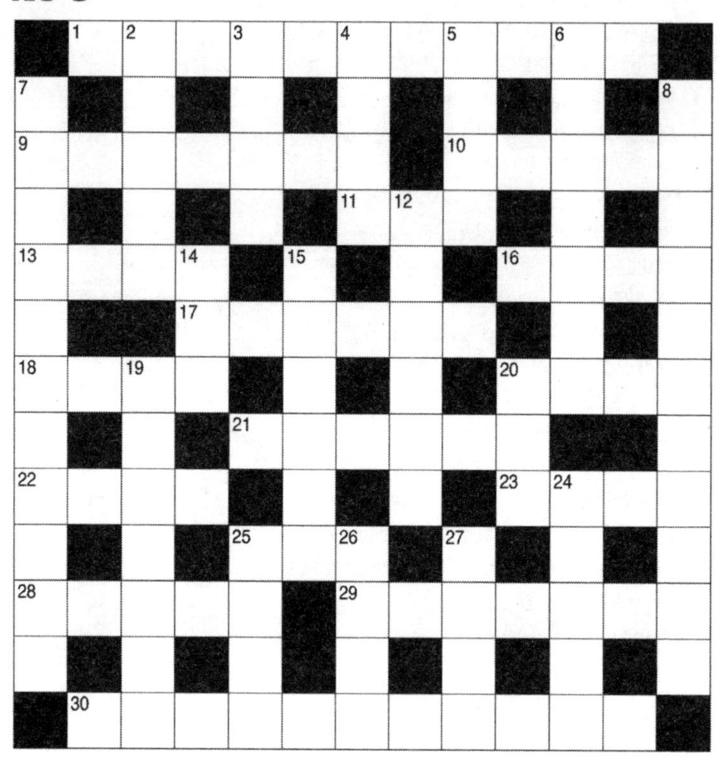

Across

1 Criminals *(1 Timothy 1:9)* (11)
9 Disregard *(Luke 11:42)* (7)
10 'If we endure, we will also — with him' *(2 Timothy 2:12)* (5)
11 'Make them — down in groups of about fifty each' *(Luke 9:14)* (3)
13 Lazily (4)
16 He was killed by his brother Cain *(Genesis 4:8)* (4)
17 Consented *(Acts 15:25)* (6)
18 A bird the Israelites were forbidden to eat *(Leviticus 11:13–15)* (4)
20 'The water had risen and was deep enough to — in' *(Ezekiel 47:5)* (4)
21 Counsel *(2 Samuel 17:11)* (6)

22 He sold his birthright to his twin brother for some red stew *(Genesis 25:30–33)* (4)
23 Those who 'practise magic — ' are twice condemned in the closing chapters of the Bible *(Revelation 21:8; 22:15)* (4)
25 Gamble (3)
28 Shows wedding guests to their seats (5)
29 Uriah, Bathsheba's husband, was one *(2 Samuel 11:3)* (7)
30 'The statutes of the Lord are — , making wise the simple' *(Psalm 19:7)* (11)

Down

2 Gabriel was one *(Luke 1:19)* (5)
3 'That on the cross my burden gladly bearing, he — and died to take away my sin' (4)
4 'A man ought to examine himself before he — the bread and drinks the cup' *(1 Corinthians 11:28)* (4)
5 Twentieth-century US composer of more than 200 Christian songs, — Kaiser (4)
6 Sign in the sky of the covenant between God and the earth *(Genesis 9:13)* (7)
7 Sinful *(2 Peter 2:9)* (11)
8 Perfect *(Hebrews 9:14)* (11)
12 In rice (anag.) (6)
14 Tibetan ox (3)
15 22 Across had one against his brother for stealing from him his father's blessing *(Genesis 27:41)* (6)
19 'When evening comes, you say, "It will be fair — , for the sky is red"' *(Matthew 16:2)* (7)
20 'The — is his, for he made it, and his hands formed the dry land' *(Psalm 95:5)* (3)
24 First Director General of the BBC, Sir John — (5)
25 Male siblings (abbrev.) (4)
26 What (anag.) (4)
27 'Mockers — up a city, but wise men turn away anger' *(Proverbs 29:8)* (4)

No 6

Across

1 Sense of right and wrong *(1 Corinthians 8:7)* (10)

7 Coming *(John 11:17)* (7)

8 'All I have is — , and all you have is mine' *(John 17:10)* (5)

10 Smarten *(Acts 9:34)* (4)

11 Hold back *(Job 9:13)* (8)

13 Member of the Society of Friends (6)

15 At ague (anag.) (6)

17 Citizen of the Greek capital (8)

18 So be it *(Galatians 6:18)* (4)

21 Twentieth-century poet and dramatist who wrote *Murder in the Cathedral*, T.S. — (5)

22 Empowers *(Philippians 3:21)* (7)
23 Imposing *(1 Samuel 9:2)* (10)

Down

1 Healed *(Luke 7:21)* (5)
2 Central space in a church (4)
3 Co-founder of Spring Harvest and General Secretary of the Evangelical Alliance 1983–97, Clive — (6)
4 Moses killed one when he saw him beating a Hebrew labourer *(Exodus 2:12)* (8)
5 Bravery *(Acts 4:13)* (7)
6 It interrupted Paul and Silas singing hymns in a Philippian jail *(Acts 16:26)* (10)
9 Transgression *(Psalm 36:1)* (10)
12 Irish province in which Dublin is situated (8)
14 Same hit (anag.) (7)
16 'The Spirit of God was hovering over the — ' *(Genesis 1:2)* (6)
19 Author of the immortal stories of Winnie the Pooh, A.A. — (5)
20 Cab (4)

No 7

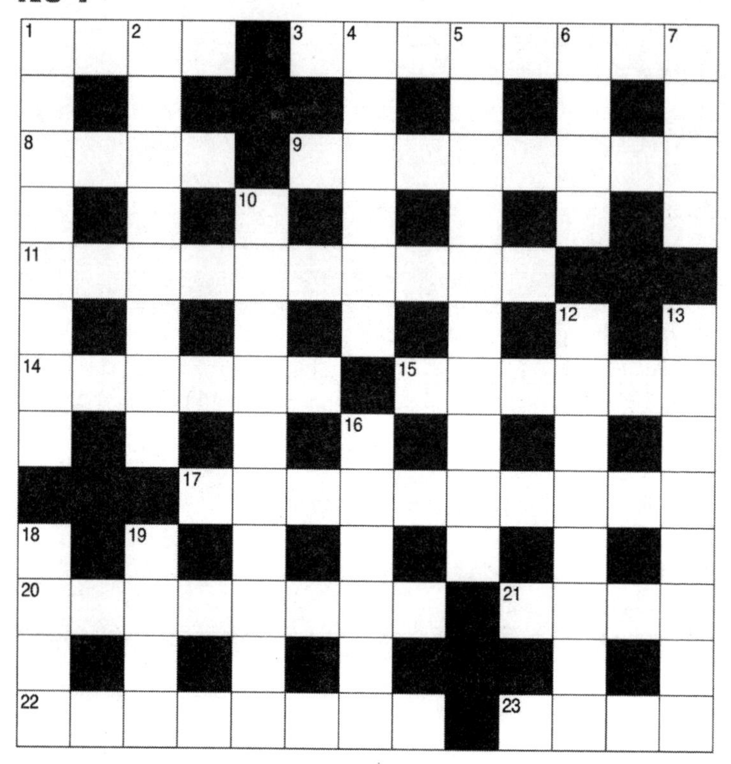

Across

1 See 23 Across

3 Where the thief on the cross was told he would be, with Jesus *(Luke 23:43)* (8)

8 Invalid (4)

9 Blasphemed *(Ezekiel 36:20)* (8)

11 Adhering to the letter of the law rather than its spirit *(Philippians 3:6)* (10)

14 Shut *(Ecclesiastes 12:4)* (6)

15 'This is how it will be with anyone who — up things for himself but is not rich towards God' *(Luke 12:21)* (6)

17 Mary on Isis (anag.) (10)

20 Agreement *(Hebrews 9:15)* (8)

21 Native of, say, Bangkok (4)

22 Deaf fort (anag.) (5-3)

23 and **1 Across** 'The Lord God took the man and put him in the Garden of — to work it and take — of it' *(Genesis 2:15)* (4,4)

Down

1 Struggle between opposing forces *(Habakkuk 1:3)* (8)

2 James defined this as 'looking after orphans and widows in their distress and keeping oneself from being polluted by the world' *(James 1:27)* (8)

4 'The one I kiss is the man; — him' *(Matthew 26:48)* (6)

5 'Be joyful in hope, patient in — , faithful in prayer' *(Romans 12:12)* (10)

6 St Columba's burial place (4)

7 Swirling current of water (4)

10 Loyalty *(Isaiah 19:18)* (10)

12 'God was pleased through the foolishness of what was — , to save those who believe' *(1 Corinthians 1:21)* (8)

13 Camp where the angel of the Lord slew 185,000 men one night *(2 Kings 19:35)* (8)

16 'There is still — — — Jonathan; he is crippled in both feet' *(2 Samuel 9:3)* (1,3,2)

18 David Livingstone was one (4)

19 Driver and Vehicle Licensing Authority (1,1,1,1)

No 8

Across

8 Academic who studies history of one of Israel's perennial enemies (13)

9 Take to court *(Matthew 5:40)* (3)

10 Absence of guilt *(1 Kings 8:32)* (9)

11 Of Tim (anag.) (5)

13 Deprive priest of ecclesiastical status (7)

16 Where Paul and Barnabas called en route from Perga to Antioch *(Acts 14:25–26)* (7)

19 'The earth is the — , and everything in it' *(Psalm 24:1)* (5)

22 'Do not neglect your gift, which was given you through a — message when the body of elders laid their hands on you' *(1 Timothy 4:14)* (9)

24 Raincoat (abbrev.) (3)
25 Issue relating to sexual ethics dealt with in the controversial Papal Encyclical *Humanae Vitae* in 1968 (13)

Down

1 'The Son of Man did not come to be served, but to serve, and to give his life as a — for many' *(Matthew 20:28)* (6)
2 Upward slope *(Nehemiah 3:19)* (6)
3 'God blessed them and said to them, "Be — and increase in number"' *(Genesis 1:28)* (8)
4 'What God has — together, let man not separate' *(Matthew 19:6)* (6)
5 One of the partners which, with BEA, formed British Airways (1,1,1,1)
6 'This will be a — — you. You will find a baby wrapped in cloths and lying in a manger' *(Luke 2:12)* (4,2)
7 Takers (anag.) (6)
12 'But the things that come — of the mouth come from the heart, and these make a man "unclean"' *(Matthew 15:18)* (3)
14 'Then I set bowls — of wine and some — before the men of the Recabite family' *(Jeremiah 35:5)* (4,4)
15 Levitical eating laws were much concerned about animals 'that chew the — ' *(Leviticus 11:3)* (3)
16 Llama-like animal noted for its wool (6)
17 The seed which fell among these was choked by them as it grew *(Luke 8:7)* (6)
18 Launch an assault against *(Genesis 14:15)* (6)
20 'Neither can you bear fruit unless you — in me' *(John 15:4)* (6)
21 John says of the healing of the royal official's son, 'This was the — miraculous sign that Jesus performed' *(John 4:54)* (6)
23 Inflict pain on *(Acts 7:26)* (4)

No 9

Across

1 Of Moses (6)

4 'You have been weighed on the — and found wanting' *(Daniel 5:27)* (6)

7 Where Jesus performed the first of his miraculous signs *(John 2:11)* (4)

8 Roman emperor who ordered all the Jews to leave Rome *(Acts 18:2)* (8)

9 Member of a conservative Jewish party in the Sanhedrin which believed there was no resurrection *(Acts 23:8)* (8)

13 South London Mission (1,1,1)

16 Sure of one's own ability *(2 Corinthians 11:17)* (4-9)

17 'At this the man's face fell. He went away — , because he had great wealth' *(Mark 10:22)* (3)
19 Airs used (anag.) (8)
24 'The Lord is my — , I shall not be in want' *(Psalm 23:1)* (8)
25 'He has sent me to — up the broken-hearted' *(Isaiah 61:1)* (4)
26 At or towards the rear of a ship (6)
27 Cross-carrying evangelist and world traveller, — Blessitt (6)

Down

1 Ridicule *(Luke 18:32)* (4)
2 Encased in strapped-on light shoes *(Song of Songs 7:1)* (9)
3 Cambridge Inter-Collegiate Christian Union (1,1,1,1,1)
4 'Father, give me my — of your estate' *(Luke 15:12)* (5)
5 Assistant (4)
6 On a par *(John 5:18)* (5)
10 Credo (anag.) (5)
11 Beaten with a rod (5)
12 The fourth of Job's 'comforters', who deferred making his contribution because of his junior status *(Job 32:6)* (5)
13 Chosen as a temple attendant, he was described by Ezra as 'a capable man' *(Ezra 8:18)* (9)
14 'Do not store up for yourselves treasures on earth, where — and rust destroy' *(Matthew 6:19)* (4)
15 Employs (4)
18 Associated with penitence for sins, along with sackcloth *(Matthew 11:21)* (5)
20 Association of South-East Asian Nations (1,1,1,1,1)
21 Sub-continent to which Baptist missionary pioneer William Carey devoted his life (5)
22 Recess at east end of a church (4)
23 One of the nine sons of Beriah *(1 Chronicles 8:15)* (4)

No 10

Across

1 'Through [Christ] we have gained — by faith into this grace' *(Romans 5:2)* (6)

4 Deprives of sight *(Deuteronomy 16:19)* (6)

8 The words of a hymn do this (mostly) (5)

9 Faithful allegiance *(1 Chronicles 12:33)* (7)

10 Belgium's chief port (7)

11 Where John was baptizing 'because there was plenty of water' *(John 3:23)* (5)

12 Imposing height *(Psalm 48:2)* (9)

17 Jesus' tempter in the wilderness *(Mark 1:13)* (5)

19 Comes between Amos and Jonah (7)

21 'Your will be done — — as it is in heaven' *(Matthew 6:10)* (2,5)

22 Gale *(Matthew 8:24)* (5)

23 Axle, eh? (anag.) (6)

24 'Out of the — I cry to you, O Lord' *(Psalm 130:1)* (6)

Down

1 Popular Christian author and humorist, — Plass (6)

2 Transparent ice-like mineral *(Revelation 4:6)* (7)

3 Method of compelling surrender by surrounding target of attack *(2 Chronicles 32:1)* (5)

5 Expose *(Isaiah 52:10)* (3,4)

6 Lonny (anag.) (5)

7 Utterance *(1 Timothy 1:15)* (6)

9 Husband of Deborah, the prophetess *(Judges 4:4)* (9)

13 Burial service *(Jeremiah 34:5)* (7)

14 What Christ threatened to do to the lukewarm church in Laodicea *(Revelation 3:16)* (4,3)

15 'Simon Peter climbed aboard and dragged the net — ' *(John 21:11)* (6)

16 His response to Jesus' decision to return to Judea was 'Let us also go, that we may die with him' *(John 11:16)* (6)

18 'There will be weeping and gnashing of — ' *(Matthew 8:12)* (5)

20 Walkway between rows of pews in a church (5)

No 11

Across

1 'Those who were standing near Paul said, "You — to insult God's high priest?"' *(Acts 23:4)* (4)

3 They were assigned to guard the tree of life *(Genesis 3:24)* (8)

9 'Elkanah son of Jeroham, the son of Elihu, the — of — , the son of Zuph, an Ephraimite' *(1 Samuel 1:1)* (3,4)

10 Surrender *(Joshua 24:23)* (5)

11 Where American livestock can be reared (5)

12 Listen (anag.) (6)

14 Alternative name for Kiriath Jearim *(2 Samuel 6:2)* (6,2,5)

17 He founded Westminster Abbey, — the Confessor (6)

19 Hebrew word for the place of the dead (5)

22 Allies of Persia in the fifth century BC *(Esther 1:3)* (5)

23 Where John Wesley was forced to preach a lot (4,3)
24 Rebellion against God; abandonment of religious belief (8)
25 Note (anag.) (4)

Down

1 Give an account of *(Mark 4:30)* (8)
2 'I — — the path of your commands, for you have set my heart free' *(Psalm 119:32)* (3,2)
4 'He took the ephod, the other — — and the carved image' *(Judges 18:20)* (9,4)
5 'You are a chosen people, a — priesthood' *(1 Peter 2:9)* (5)
6 The meek, the merciful and the mourners are all this *(Matthew 5:4–5, 7)* (7)
7 Musical Instrument Digital Interface (1,1,1,1)
8 He was the son of Nun *(Deuteronomy 34:9)* (6)
13 'Let the little — come to me' *(Matthew 19:14)* (8)
15 'About three thousand were — — their number that day' *(Acts 2:41)* (5,2)
16 In John's vision, the wall of the new Jerusalem was made of this *(Revelation 21:18)* (6)
18 'Our citizenship is in heaven. And we eagerly — a Saviour from there, the Lord Jesus Christ' *(Philippians 3:20)* (5)
20 'Glorify the Lord with me: let us — his name together' *(Psalm 34:3)* (5)
21 Young Men's Christian Association (1,1,1,1)

No 12

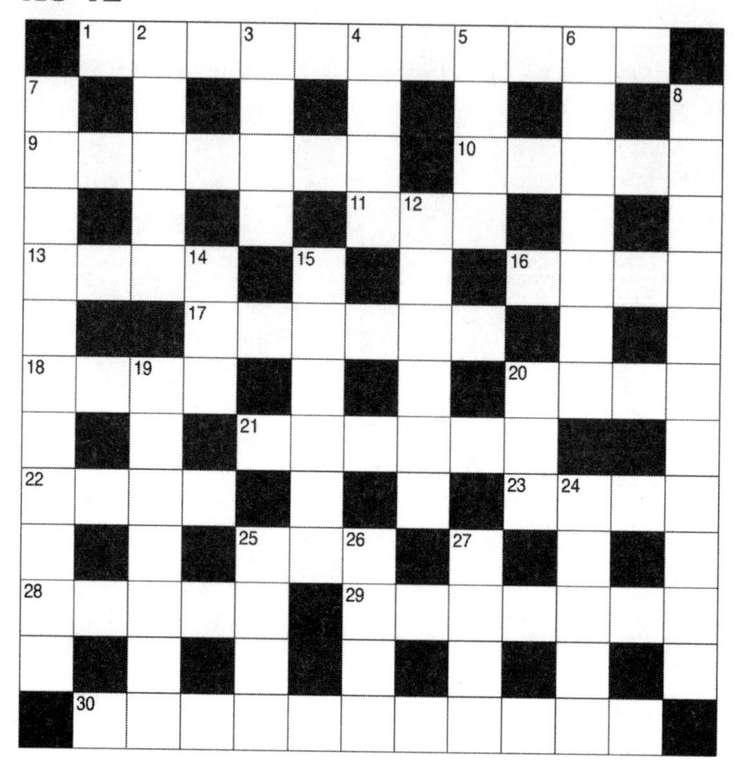

Across

1 and **20 Down** 'Lord of all — , Lord of all — , whose trust, ever child-like, no cares could destroy' (11,3)

9 Moses' question to a fighting Hebrew labourer: 'Why are you — your fellow Hebrew?' *(Exodus 2:13)* (7)

10 Acclaimed cellist who contracted multiple sclerosis at the height of her fame, Jacqueline — (2,3)

11 'At even — the sun was set, the sick, O Lord, around thee lay' (3)

13 A descendant of Gad *(Numbers 26:16)* (4)

16 'Do not leave Jerusalem, but — for the gift my Father promised' *(Acts 1:4)* (4)

17 Clambers *(Jeremiah 48:44)* (6)

18 Peter's response to questioning by the Sanhedrin: 'We must — God rather than men!' *(Acts 5:29)* (4)
20 Christian paraplegic author, artist and campaigner, — Eareckson Tada (4)
21 Bird partial to the nests of other birds (6)
22 'Such large crowds gathered round him that he got into a boat and sat — —' *(Matthew 13:2)* (2,2)
23 Infectious tropical disease (4)
25 Tree (3)
28 'No fear of me should — you, nor should my hand be heavy upon you' *(Job 33:7)* (5)
29 For example, to Titus, Timothy or Philemon (7)
30 Week beginning with Pentecost Sunday, according to the Church's calendar (11)

Down

2 'O Jerusalem... how — I have longed to gather your children together' *(Matthew 23:37)* (5)
3 Way out (4)
4 Exhort *(Romans 12:1)* (4)
5 Done (anag.) (4)
6 Highest of the four voice-parts in a choir (7)
7 Concerning the study of God (11)
8 Uniquely, it has Abbey, Cathedral and Chapel (11)
12 Admonish *(Matthew 16:22)* (6)
14 Frozen (3)
15 Established form of religious ceremony (6)
19 Inscription often found on gravestones (7)
20 See 1 Across
24 Behaved *(Joshua 7:1)* (5)
25 Time (anag.) (4)
26 Lists choice of meals (4)
27 'For the wages of sin is death, but the — of God is eternal life in Christ Jesus our Lord' *(Romans 6:23)* (4)

No 13

Across

1 Provisional meeting place of God and the Jews *(Exodus 25:9)* (10)

7 David's third son, killed when his head got caught in a tree during a battle with his father *(2 Samuel 18:14–15)* (7)

8 They ruled much of the west coast of South America in the 15th and early 16th centuries (5)

10 Small deer of European and Asian extraction (4)

11 Seized control of *(Numbers 21:25)* (8)

13 Terror *(Luke 24:5)* (6)

15 First World War heroine shot by the Germans in Brussels, Nurse Edith — (6)

17 Stormy (8)

18 A bitter variety of this, together with lamb and unleavened bread, was the Passover menu for anyone 'unclean' *(Numbers 9:11)* (4)

21 Arson (anag.) (5)

22 How John Newton described God's grace in his well-known hymn (7)

23 Habitation *(Isaiah 27:10)* (10)

Down

1 ' — and see that the Lord is good' *(Psalm 34:8)* (5)

2 'The wicked man flees though no one pursues, but the righteous are as — as a lion' *(Proverbs 28:1)* (4)

3 One of the exiles, a descendant of Parosh, who married a foreign woman *(Ezra 10:25)* (6)

4 He escaped from Nob when Saul killed the rest of his family and joined David *(1 Samuel 22:19–20)* (8)

5 City and lake in Central Switzerland (7)

6 'Offer your bodies as living — , holy and pleasing to God' *(Romans 12:1)* (10)

9 Pouches carried by horses *(Genesis 49:14)* (10)

12 One who accepts government by God (8)

14 Aromatic substance commonly used in Jewish ritual *(Exodus 30:1)* (7)

16 He asked Jesus, 'What is truth?' *(John 18:38)* (6)

19 Are *(Romans 13:1)* (5)

20 'You are to give him the name Jesus, because he will — his people from their sins' *(Matthew 1:21)* (4)

No 14

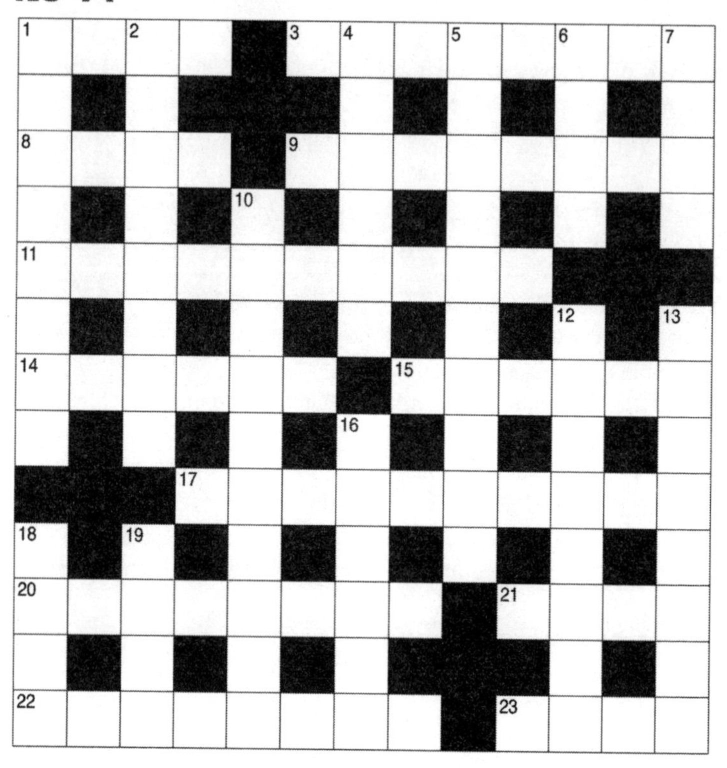

Across

1 'Again Peter denied it, and at that moment a — began to crow' *(John 18:27)* (4)

3 Fetters *(Job 33:11)* (8)

8 Perform on a musical instrument *(1 Samuel 16:23)* (4)

9 Paul describes it as 'the third heaven' *(2 Corinthians 12:2–4)* (8)

11 Loyally *(Deuteronomy 11:13)* (10)

14 Hens? Me? (anag.) (6)

15 Not visible *(Matthew 6:6)* (6)

17 Predicted site of the final great battle *(Revelation 16:16)* (10)

20 Jacob's youngest son *(Genesis 35:18)* (8)

21 One of Zophar's eleven sons *(1 Chronicles 7:36)* (4)

22 For example, London, Paris, Rome (8)
23 United Society for the Propagation of the Gospel (1,1,1,1)

Down

1 Favourite church activity: Fellowship round a — — — (3,2,3)
2 Divinely bestowed powers or talents (8)
4 Pile together *(1 Thessalonians 2:16)* (4,2)
5 Commanded to justify *(John 8:13)* (10)
6 Timothy's grandmother *(2 Timothy 1:5)* (4)
7 Killed *(Psalm 78:34)* (4)
10 One of Graham Kendrick's best-known songs, — — King (3,7)
12 Indecency *(Mark 7:22)* (8)
13 Unceasing *(Jeremiah 15:18)* (8)
16 He prophesied 'the abomination that causes desolation' *(Matthew 24:15)* (6)
18 British Board of Film Classification (1,1,1,1)
19 Pans (anag.) (4)

No 15

Across

8 Interrogated *(Acts 12:19)* (5-8)

9 'Burn it in a wood fire on the — heap' *(Leviticus 4:12)* (3)

10 Tobit, Judith, Baruch and the books of Esdras and the Maccabees are part of it (9)

11 Science fiction (abbrev.) (3-2)

13 Clay pit (anag.) (7)

16 Went to *(John 4:46)* (7)

19 'Therefore, I urge you, brothers, in view of God's mercy, to — your bodies as living sacrifices' *(Romans 12:1)* (5)

22 David's plea to God concerning those referred to in 14 Down: 'On — — let them escape' *(Psalm 56:7)* (2,7)

24 Royal Automobile Club (1,1,1)
25 How the book of Ezekiel refers to God more than 200 times *(Ezekiel 2:4)* (9,4)

Down

1 Seas *(Proverbs 8:24)* (6)
2 One of the sons of Eli the priest, killed in battle by the Philistines *(1 Samuel 4:11)* (6)
3 Specialist in the study of the Muslim religion (8)
4 'Do not rebuke an older man harshly, but — him as if he were your father' *(1 Timothy 5:1)* (6)
5 One of Esau's grandsons *(Genesis 36:11)* (4)
6 Taking a chance (colloq.) (2,4)
7 God's instructions to the Israelites concerning grain offerings: ' — salt to — your offerings' *(Leviticus 2:13)* (3,3)
12 Confederation of British Industry (1,1,1)
14 'All day long they twist my words; they are always — to harm me' *(Psalm 56:5)* (8)
15 The crowd's reaction to Jesus bringing back to life a widow's son in Nain *(Luke 7:16)* (3)
16 Disappear *(Psalm 104:35)* (6)
17 How Jeremiah was likely to die if he wasn't rescued from the cistern where he was imprisoned *(Jeremiah 38:9)* (6)
18 What the prophets do to a wall, with whitewash *(Ezekiel 13:10, RSV)* (4,2)
20 Made by a plough *(Job 39:10)* (6)
21 Noah was relieved when the flood waters continued to — *(Genesis 8:5)* (6)
23 Jesus gave the Twelve the power and authority to do this to diseases *(Luke 9:1)* (4)

No 16

Across

1 The earth is one (6)
4 'On a hill far away stood an old — cross' (6)
7 'I am the — vine and my Father is the gardener' *(John 15:1)* (4)
8 The Caesar who was Roman Emperor at the time of Jesus' birth *(Luke 2:1)* (8)
9 'Your — should be the same as that of Christ Jesus' *(Philippians 2:5)* (8)
13 Jesus said that no one would put a lighted lamp under this *(Luke 8:16)* (3)
16 Involvement *(1 Corinthians 10:16)* (13)
17 Armed conflict *(2 Chronicles 15:19)* (3)
19 Where the Gaderene pigs were feeding *(Mark 5:11)* (8)

24 What jeering youths called Elisha on the road to Bethel *(2 Kings 2:23)* (8)
25 The Venerable — , eighth-century Jarrow ecclesiastical scholar (4)
26 8 Across issued a decree that this should take place *(Luke 2:1)* (6)
27 Come into prominence *(Deuteronomy 13:13)* (6)

Down

1 Where some of the seed scattered by the sower fell *(Matthew 13:4)* (4)
2 Sexually immoral person whom God will judge *(Hebrews 13:4)* (9)
3 Gospel leaflet (5)
4 Physical state of the boy brought to Jesus for healing *(Mark 9:18)* (5)
5 Tugs (anag.) (4)
6 To put forth (5)
10 Nationality associated with St Patrick (5)
11 Leader of the descendants of Kohath *(1 Chronicles 15:5)* (5)
12 'After this, his brother came out, with his hand grasping — heel' *(Genesis 25:26)* (5)
13 At Dothan the Lord struck the Arameans with — at Elisha's request *(2 Kings 6:18)* (9)
14 'Peter, before the cock crows today, you will — three times that you know me' *(Luke 22:34)* (4)
15 Spit out *(Psalm 59:7)* (4)
18 'When I — , I am still with you' *(Psalm 139:18)* (5)
20 Concepts *(Acts 17:20)* (5)
21 Thyatira's dealer in purple cloth *(Acts 16:14)* (5)
22 Does (anag.) (4)
23 The second set of seven cows in Pharaoh's dream were this *(Genesis 41:19)* (4)

No 17

Across

1 Relating to the whole universe (6)

4 The disciple who made the remark in 8 Across *(John 20:24)* (6)

8 'Unless I see the nail marks — — hands, I will not believe it' *(John 20:25)* (2,3)

9 He urged King Jehoiakim not to burn the scroll containing Jeremiah's message *(Jeremiah 36:25)* (7)

10 Baptist minister and controversial founder of America's Moral Majority, Jerry — (7)

11 'Look, here is — . Why shouldn't I be baptized?' *(Acts 8:36)* (5)

12 Repossessed *(Genesis 14:16)* (9)

17 Port from which Paul sailed on his last journey to Rome *(Acts 27:3–4)* (5)

19 'Moses was not aware that his face was — because he had spoken with the Lord' *(Exodus 34:29)* (7)

21 Roonwit, C.S. Lewis's half-man, half-horse (7)

22 Grill *(Luke 24:42)* (5)

23 'The lot fell to Matthias; so he was added to the — apostles' *(Acts 1:26)* (6)

24 'I was sick and you looked after me, I was in — and you came to visit me' *(Matthew 25:36)* (6)

Down

1 Coastal rockfaces *(Psalm 141:6)* (6)

2 Academic *(1 Corinthians 1:20)* (7)

3 Publish *(Daniel 6:26)* (5)

5 For example, the Crusades (4,3)

6 11 Across is certainly this (5)

7 He reps (anag.) (6)

9 Liberator *(Psalm 18:2)* (9)

13 Man who asked the question in 11 Across was in charge of all her treasury *(Acts 8:27)* (7)

14 They must be 'worthy of respect, sincere, not indulging in much wine' *(1 Timothy 3:8)* (7)

15 The human mind or soul (6)

16 'O Lord, while precious children starve, the tools of war increase; their bread is — ' (Graham Kendrick) (6)

18 'We played the flute for you, and you did not — ' *(Matthew 11:17)* (5)

20 Bared (anag.) (5)

No 18

Across

1 'Therefore let us — passing judgment on one another' *(Romans 14:13)* (4)

3 'I — — these persons here present' (Marriage service) (4,4)

9 According to a prearranged timetable *(Numbers 28:3)* (7)

10 Group of eight (5)

11 The cell into which the Philippian jailer put Paul and Silas *(Acts 16:24)* (5)

12 — Taylor, pioneer missionary to China (6)

14 Otherwise known as the Eucharist, Breaking of Bread, the Lord's Table (4,9)

17 'So that after I have preached to others, I — will not be disqualified for the prize' *(1 Corinthians 9:27)* (6)

19 Attend to (3,2)
22 Approximately *(Acts 4:4)* (5)
23 Tea rite (anag.) (7)
24 Rule of sovereign (8)
25 Test (anag.) (4)

Down

1 The name of the street where Judas lived in Damascus and where Saul of Tarsus stayed *(Acts 9:11)* (8)
2 'The playing of the merry — , sweet singing in the choir' (5)
4 'We have been saying that — — was credited to him as righteous' *(Romans 4:9)* (8,5)
5 Dr Martyn — Jones, famous for his ministry at Westminster Chapel (5)
6 Port at which Paul landed on his way to Rome *(Acts 28:13)* (7)
7 Observe *(Ruth 3:4)* (4)
8 Minister of religion (6)
13 'I am — of this man's blood. It is your responsibility' *(Matthew 27:24)* (8)
15 'Greater love has no one than this, that he — — his life for his friends' *(John 15:13)* (3,4)
16 Archbishop who calculated that the world began in 4004BC (6)
18 'No one can — the kingdom of God unless he is born of water and the Spirit' *(John 3:5)* (5)
20 Establish by law (5)
21 Product of Gilead noted for its healing properties *(Jeremiah 46:11)* (4)

No 19

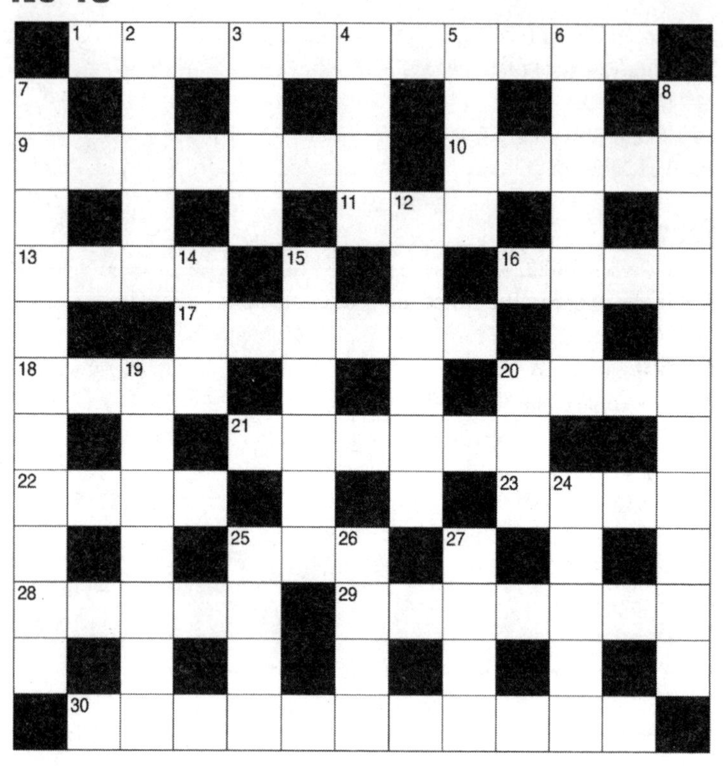

Across

1 'Eloi, Eloi, lama — ?' *(Matthew 27:46)* (11)

9 Joseph's second son *(Genesis 41:52)* (7)

10 'No one sews a — of unshrunk cloth on an old garment' *(Mark 2:21)* (5)

11 See 3 Down (3)

13 Cultivate *(2 Samuel 9:10)* (4)

16 Not firm or stiff *(Proverbs 26:7)* (4)

17 Jacob's second wife *(Genesis 29:28)* (6)

18 On Her Majesty's Service (1,1,1,1)

20 'As for us, why do we endanger ourselves every hour? — — every day, I mean that, brothers' *(1 Corinthians 15:30–31)* (1,3)

21 The second son that Leah bore to Jacob *(Genesis 29:33)* (6)

22 Piece of work *(Acts 20:24)* (4)

23 The expensive perfume that Mary poured on Jesus' feet at Bethany *(John 12:3)* (4)

25 'Come and — the place where he lay' *(Matthew 28:6)* (3)

28 Vegetable identified by the Israelites in the desert as one they remembered enjoying in Egypt *(Numbers 11:5)* (5)

29 'But the — of this life and the deceitfulness of wealth choke it' *(Matthew 13:22)* (7)

30 It happened to Paul three times *(2 Corinthians 11:25)* (11)

Down

2 The second son that Leah's servant Zilpah bore to Jacob *(Genesis 30:13)* (5)

3 and **11 Across** Parents of Cain *(Genesis 4:1)* (4,3)

4 Abode *(Luke 4:38)* (4)

5 'Now faith is being sure of what we — for' *(Hebrews 11:1)* (4)

6 'When they entered [the tomb], they did — — the body of the Lord Jesus' *(Luke 24:3)* (3,4)

7 The last-named fruit of the Spirit *(Galatians 5:22–23)* (4-7)

8 Woman who looks after sheep *(Genesis 29:9)* (11)

12 Looked at *(Numbers 32:9)* (6)

14 Form of address to married woman (3)

15 Baruch was so described *(Jeremiah 36:26)* (6)

19 Andrew told his brother Simon that they had found him *(John 1:41)* (7)

20 Where the Good Samaritan took the man attacked by robbers on the Jericho road *(Luke 10:34)* (3)

24 'This son of mine was dead and is — again; he was lost and is found' *(Luke 15:24)* (5)

25 Pins (anag.) (4)

26 Large jug or pitcher (4)

27 Rice (anag.) (4)

No 20

Across

1 Relating to the Jewish day of rest (10)

7 Point of view *(Matthew 22:17)* (7)

8 20th-century Brethren philanthropist whose construction company became one of the UK's biggest, Sir John — (5)

10 Girl's name (4)

11 Peter was accused of being one in the courtyard of the high priest's house *(Luke 22:59)* (8)

13 The fifth of the 'seven churches' *(Revelation 3:1–6)* (6)

15 'Now the famine was — in Samaria' *(1 Kings 18:2)* (6)

17 Banned by the seventh Commandment *(Exodus 20:14)* (8)

18 Insect most closely associated with itching *(1 Samuel 24:14)* (4)

21 Bantu tribe which gives its name to tiny landlocked country in southern Africa (5)

22 Familiar material in churches that use an overhead projector (7)

23 Last book of the Bible (10)

Down

1 The young David's favourite weapon *(1 Samuel 17:40)* (5)

2 'Your vats will — over with new wine' *(Proverbs 3:10)* (4)

3 Once yearly *(Exodus 30:10)* (6)

4 Milled it (anag.) (3-5)

5 Region north of Damascus of which Lysanias was tetrarch *(Luke 3:1)* (7)

6 Comes between Philippians and 1 Thessalonians (10)

9 Lake where the first disciples were called *(Luke 5:1–11)* (10)

12 Abusive outburst (8)

14 Are loud (anag.) (7)

16 Printing errors (6)

19 'Take my yoke upon you and — from me' *(Matthew 11:29)* (5)

20 Jacob's third son *(Genesis 29:34)* (4)

No 21

Across

1 and 3 Two of the disciples who witnessed the transfiguration of Jesus *(Luke 9:28)* (4,3,5)

3 See 1 Across

8 'Let us draw — to God with a sincere heart in full assurance of faith' *(Hebrews 10:22)* (4)

9 O Simon is (anag.) (8)

11 Form of government under the direct rule of God or his agents (10)

14 How Jesus found his disciples when he returned to them after praying in Gethsemane *(Luke 22:45)* (6)

15 In *The Pilgrim's Progress*, the name of the meadow into which Christian strayed, which led to Doubting Castle (2-4)

17 Glad sin rat (anag.) (10)

20 Spinal column *(Leviticus 3:9)* (8)
21 Valley of the Balsam Tree with a reputation of being a waterless place *(Psalm 84:6)* (4)
22 'The oracle of Balaam son of Beor, the oracle of one — — sees clearly' *(Numbers 24:3)* (5,3)
23 Adam and Eve's third son *(Genesis 4:25)* (4)

Down

1 David's great friend *(1 Samuel 20:17)* (8)
2 'The Lord… will bring me safely to his — kingdom' *(2 Timothy 4:18)* (8)
4 'I, Daniel, mourned for three weeks. I ate no choice food; — — or wine touched my lips' *(Daniel 10:3)* (2,4)
5 Seeking to vindicate *(Job 32:2)* (10)
6 Female servant *(Isaiah 24:2)* (4)
7 'For Christ died for — once for all' *(1 Peter 3:18)* (4)
10 'Offering spiritual sacrifices — to God through Jesus Christ' *(1 Peter 2:5)* (10)
12 Jesus said that some people had renounced this 'because of the kingdom of heaven' *(Matthew 19:12)* (8)
13 One of the three men thrown into the furnace for refusing to worship Nebuchadnezzar's golden image *(Daniel 3:20)* (8)
16 'You have — of good things laid up for many years. Take life easy; eat, drink and be merry' *(Luke 12:19)* (6)
18 'There before me was a white horse! Its rider held — — , and he was given a crown' *(Revelation 6:2)* (1,3)
19 Equipment to Charity Hospitals Overseas (1,1,1,1)

No 22

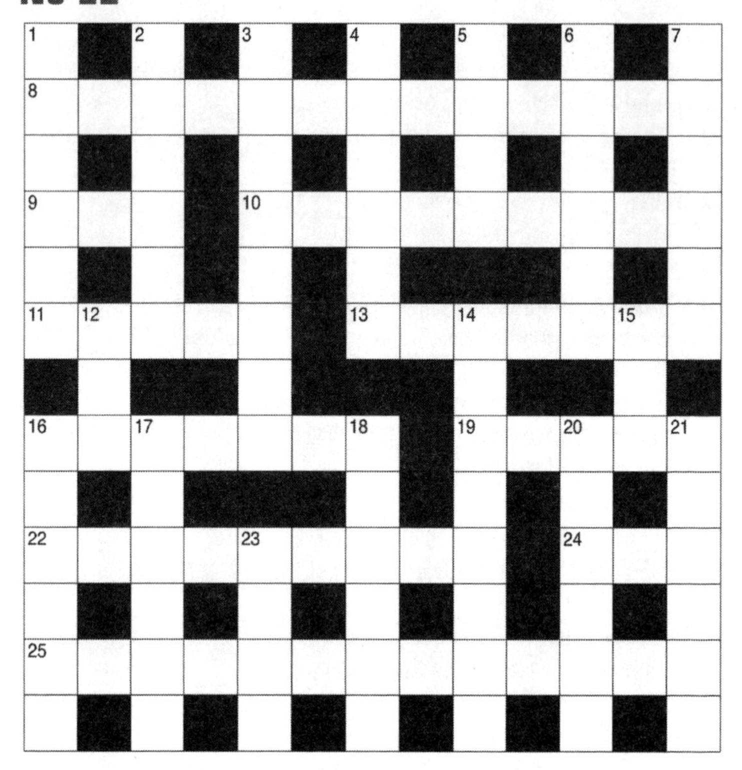

Across

8 Where the ark of the covenant was kept for 20 years *(1 Samuel 7:1)* (7,6)

9 One of the parts of the body on which blood and oil were put in the ritual cleansing from infectious skin diseases *(Leviticus 14:14–17)* (3)

10 Uncomfortable (3,2,4)

11 'Yet I have loved Jacob, but Esau I have — ' *(Malachi 1:3)* (5)

13 Where Paul said farewell to the elders of the church in Ephesus *(Acts 20:17)* (7)

16 'Jesus bent down and — to write on the ground with his finger' *(John 8:6)* (7)

19 Prophet from Moresheth *(Jeremiah 26:18)* (5)

22 Comes between Exodus and Numbers (9)

24 and **2 Down** 'Then Elkanah went home to Ramah, but the boy ministered before the Lord under — the — ' *(1 Samuel 2:11)* (3,6)

25 There was no room for them in the inn *(Luke 2:7)* (4,3,6)

Down

1 Rough drawing *(2 Kings 16:10)* (6)

2 See 24 Across

3 Underground literature (including Christian books) circulated in the Soviet Union (8)

4 Lo, mash (anag.) (6)

5 The Bible's shortest verse: 'Jesus — ' *(John 11:35)* (4)

6 'Can a mother forget the baby at her — and have no compassion on the child she has borne?' *(Isaiah 49:15)* (6)

7 Can be seen in a dying fire *(Psalm 102:3)* (6)

12 'Send me, therefore, a man... experienced in the — of engraving, to work in Judah and Jerusalem' *(2 Chronicles 2:7)* (3)

14 Second city of Cyprus (8)

15 United Nations Association (1,1,1)

16 One of the women who first heard that Jesus had risen from the dead *(Mark 16:1)* (6)

17 Braved (anag.) (6)

18 — of Evangelism, outreach initiative in the 1990s (6)

20 'Woe to those who are wise in their own eyes and — in their own sight' *(Isaiah 5:21)* (6)

21 'Neither — nor depth... will be able to separate us from the love of God' *(Romans 8:39)* (6)

23 What Jesus shed in 5 Down (4)

No 23

Across

1 He must be 'the husband of but one wife and must manage his children and his household well' *(1 Timothy 3:12)* (6)

4 'For we must all — before the judgement seat of Christ' *(2 Corinthians 5:10)* (6)

7 'They reeled and staggered like drunken men; they were at their — end' *(Psalm 107:27)* (4)

8 See 19 Across

9 It concerned who among the disciples would be the greatest *(Luke 9:46)* (8)

13 Formed by the Jews in Thessalonica to root out Paul and Silas *(Acts 17:5)* (3)

16 'He has sent me to bind up the — ' *(Isaiah 61:1)* (6-7)

17 Moved rapidly on foot *(Matthew 28:8)* (3)

19 and **8** ' — a great company of the — host appeared with the angel' *(Luke 2:13)* (8,8)

24 Hindrance *(Romans 14:13)* (8)

25 Comes between Luke and Acts (4)

26 Empower *(Acts 4:29)* (6)

27 'Get these out of here! How dare you turn my Father's house into a — !' *(John 2:16)* (6)

Down

1 Sunrise *(Psalm 119:147)* (4)

2 The part of the day when Cornelius the Caesarean centurion had a vision of an angel of God *(Acts 10:3)* (9)

3 He was one of those who returned with Zerubbabel from exile in Babylon to Jerusalem *(Nehemiah 7:7)* (5)

4 'No one can see the kingdom of God unless he is born — ' *(John 3:3)* (5)

5 Animal hunted or killed as food *(Ezekiel 22:25)* (4)

6 'He encouraged them — — remain true to the Lord' *(Acts 11:23)* (3,2)

10 Ruses (anag.) (5)

11 Jewish priestly vestment *(Exodus 28:6)* (5)

12 Visible sign of what had been there *(Daniel 2:35)* (5)

13 This was the trade of Alexander, who did Paul 'a great deal of harm' *(2 Timothy 4:14)* (9)

14 'This is my — , which is for you; do this in remembrance of me' *(1 Corinthians 11:24)* (4)

15 One of Noah's great-great-grandsons *(Genesis 10:24)* (4)

18 Traditionally the first British Christian martyr (5)

20 Relationship of Ner to Saul *(1 Samuel 14:50)* (5)

21 Jacob had one at a place he named Bethel while on his way to Haran, fleeing from Esau *(Genesis 28:12)* (5)

22 Bats (anag.) (4)

23 'You strain out a — but swallow a camel' *(Matthew 23:24)* (4)

No 24

Across

1 'The Lord Jesus… took bread, and when he had given — , he broke it' *(1 Corinthians 11:24)* (6)

4 'He has taken me to the banquet hall, and his — over me is love' *(Song of Songs 2:4)* (6)

8 Surrey town that hosts the National Christian Resources Exhibition (5)

9 Also known as Abednego *(Daniel 1:7)* (7)

10 Liken *(Isaiah 40:18)* (7)

11 A son of Etam, descendant of Judah *(1 Chronicles 4:3)* (5)

12 A part of the temple where the blood of a young bull was to be smeared *(Ezekiel 45:19)* (9)

17 'They make many promises, take false — and make agreements' *(Hosea 10:4)* (5)

19 Roman province to which Paul returned after evangelizing it on his first missionary journey *(Acts 16:6)* (7)

21 Material used to make baby Moses' basket *(Exodus 2:3)* (7)

22 'And feeble as — , in thee do we trust, nor find thee to fail' (5)

23 'The watchman opens the gate for him, and the sheep — to his voice' *(John10:3)* (6)

24 Stalk carrying the sponge of wine vinegar given to Christ on the cross *(John 19:29)* (6)

Down

1 Elijah dug one round the altar he built on Mount Carmel and filled it with water *(1 Kings 18:32)* (6)

2 'I am not — of the gospel, because it is the power of God for the salvation of everyone who believes' *(Romans 1:16)* (7)

3 Buddhist term relating to belief in reincarnation (5)

5 Damascus disciple who, at God's command, restored the sight of the blinded Saul of Tarsus *(Acts 9:12)* (7)

6 and **16** Horses: their sound *(Jeremiah 50:11)* (5) and their gait *(Joel 2:4)* (6)

7 A three (anag.) (6)

9 Athenian council addressed memorably by Paul *(Acts 17:22)* (9)

13 Abide by *(Galatians 3:5)* (7)

14 Persian princes *(Daniel 3:2)* (7)

15 Force *(Galatians 6:12)* (6)

16 See 6 Down (6)

18 Paste (anag.) (5)

20 How the cedars of Lebanon are described *(Isaiah 2:13)* (5)

No 25

Across

1 'How long will you — your face from me?' *(Psalm 13:1)* (4)

3 'Let us, then, go to him outside the camp, bearing the — he bore' *(Hebrews 13:13)* (8)

9 Posh sin (anag.) *(Romans 8:15)* (7)

10 Solemn pledges *(Matthew 5:33)* (5)

11 Italian term for full orchestra (5)

12 'For he who avenges blood remembers; he does not — the cry of the afflicted' *(Psalm 9:12)* (6)

14 Prescience *(1 Peter 1:2)* (13)

17 Where a Hindu holy man lives (6)

19 'If he found any… who belonged to the Way, whether — — women, he might take them as prisoners' *(Acts 9:3)* (3,2)

22 Fragrance *(2 Corinthians 2:15)* (5)
23 Vine hen (anag.) *(Jonah 1:2)* (7)
24 Precious stone decorating the twelfth foundation of the New Jerusalem *(Revelation 21:20)* (8)
25 'Will you keep to the old path that evil men have — ?' *(Job 22:15)* (4)

Down

1 'Then Moses raised his arm and struck the rock twice with — — ' *(Numbers 20:11)* (3,5)
2 'You have heard that it was said to the people long ago, " — — murder"' *(Matthew 5:21)* (2,3)
4 One of Paul's many hardships endured as a servant of God *(2 Corinthians 6:5)* (13)
5 'We ourselves, who have the firstfruits of the Spirit, — inwardly' *(Romans 8:23)* (5)
6 Changed *(Daniel 6:8)* (7)
7 'My yoke is — and my burden is light' *(Matthew 11:30)* (4)
8 Recoil *(Revelation 12:11)* (6)
13 'O Lord, you have — me and you know me' *(Psalm 139:1)* (8)
15 ' — to me the joy of your salvation' *(Psalm 51:12)* (7)
16 Express sorrow *(Isaiah 16:7)* (6)
18 'Then he said to Thomas, " — out your hand and put it into my side"' *(John 20:27)* (5)
20 'God has said, " — will I leave you; — will I forsake you"' *(Hebrews 13:5)* (5)
21 Son of Onam and brother of Shammai *(1 Chronicles 2:28)* (4)

No 26

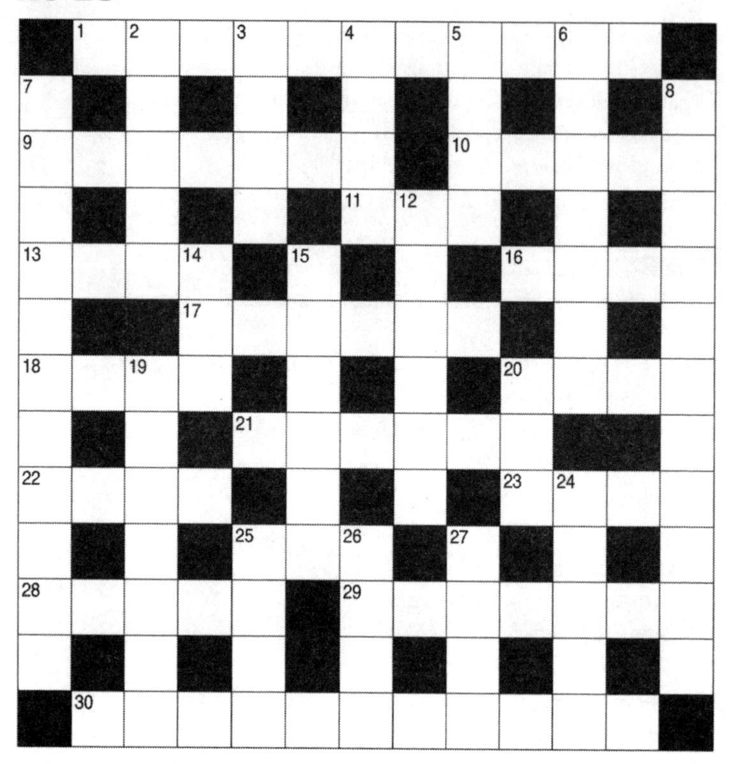

Across

1 Paul said the wrath of God 'is being revealed from heaven' against this *(Romans 1:18)* (11)

9 Go smite (anag.) (7)

10 'But — I have risen, I will go ahead of you into Galilee' *(Matthew 26:32)* (5)

11 'Take and —; this is my body' *(Matthew 26:26)* (3)

13 Type *(2 Thessalonians 2:10)* (4)

16 'Woe to those who — iniquity' *(Micah 2:1)* (4)

17 'How shall we — if we ignore such a great salvation?' *(Hebrews 2:3)* (6)

18 Opposite of evens (4)

20 Previously cited (Latin) (4)

21 'There is surely — — of God in this place, and they will kill me because of my wife' *(Genesis 20:11)* (2,4)
22 The Thessalonians were warned to keep away from every brother who was this *(2 Thessalonians 3:6)* (4)
23 Beat (anag.) (4)
25 To trouble or afflict *(Job 16:3)* (3)
28 Part of a roof *(1 Kings 7:9)* (5)
29 Attain *(Job 5:12)* (7)
30 Insect noted for its gymnastic ability *(Psalm 78:46)* (11)

Down

2 Smell *(John 11:39)* (5)
3 Lion's home *(Jeremiah 25:38)* (4)
4 'Jesus Christ is the — yesterday and today and for ever' *(Hebrews 13:8)* (4)
5 Tidy (4)
6 Made their home *(Genesis 47:27)* (7)
7 Their task was to carry the curtains of the tabernacle *(Numbers 4:25–26)* (11)
8 Timothy's was called Lois *(2 Timothy 1:5)* (11)
12 The Lover likened the fragrance of the Beloved's breath to these *(Song of Songs 7:8)* (6)
14 Times Educational Supplement (1,1,1)
15 Eight-tentacled sea creatures (6)
19 'And lead us not into temptation, but — us from the evil one' *(Matthew 6:13)* (7)
20 D.L. Moody's legendary song leader, — D. Sankey (3)
24 Rarely used musical note (5)
25 'Your will be done on earth — it — in heaven' *(Matthew 6:10)* (2,2)
26 and 27 'The Lord Almighty will — them with a — , as when he struck down Midian at the rock of Oreb' *(Isaiah 10:26)* (4,4)
27 See 26 Down

No 27

Across

1 Success or wealth *(Deuteronomy 28:11)* (10)
7 Forbidden fruit for Nazirites *(Numbers 6:3)* (7)
8 Concede *(Job 27:5)* (5)
10 Look at *(Psalm 48:13)* (4)
11 Much in evidence after weddings (8)
13 Condense *(Job 36:27)* (6)
15 Breakwater (6)
17 Give a tan (anag.) (8)
18 More usually now called Pentecost, — Sunday (4)
21 After living for 365 years, it was said of him that 'he walked with God' *(Genesis 5:23–24)* (5)

22 Trampled *(Judges 9:27)* (7)

23 For example, Miriam, Deborah *(Exodus 15:20; Judges 4:4)* (10)

Down

1 Arrogance *(Proverbs 8:13)* (5)

2 Roman poet from first century BC (4)

3 So rapt (anag.) (6)

4 Declare again *(2 Corinthians 2:8)* (8)

5 Paul's 'fellow worker', to whom he sent two epistles *(Romans 16:21)* (7)

6 God's foreseeing care and protection *(Job 10:12)* (10)

9 Traditional form of Roman Catholic Mass (10)

12 'The Lord… has given the — of Israel to David and his descendants for ever' *(2 Chronicles 13:5)* (8)

14 'My soul glorifies the Lord and my spirit rejoices in God my — ' *(Luke 1:46–47)* (7)

16 The central element in Nebuchadnezzar's dream, identified and interpreted by Daniel *(Daniel 2:31)* (6)

19 'On this rock I will build my church, and the gates of — will not overcome it' *(Matthew 16:18)* (5)

20 City where Paul was under house arrest for two years *(Acts 28:16)* (4)

No 28

Across

1 Made from the fruit of the vine, symbol of the blood of Christ (4)

3 'You are to set an ambush behind the city. Don't go very far from it. All of you be on — —' *(Joshua 8:4)* (3,5)

8 Seep (4)

9 Celebrated by Jesus on the night of his betrayal *(Luke 22:15)* (8)

11 One of the supposed sites of Christ's burial place in Jerusalem (6,4)

14 'A city on a hill — be hidden' *(Matthew 5:14)* (6)

15 He inherited Elijah's mantle *(2 Kings 2:12–13)* (6)

17 Where Jesus prayed 'Not as I will, but as you will' *(Matthew 26:36, 39)* (10)

20 'Only in his home town and in his — — is a prophet without honour' *(Matthew 13:57)* (3,5)

21 Sail (anag.) (4)
22 How Jesus was punished before his crucifixion *(Matthew 27:26)* (8)
23 Eye sore (4)

Down

1 Can't grow (anag.) (5,3)
2 A servant girl to Peter, 'You also were with that — , Jesus' *(Mark 14:67)* (8)
4 Well-being *(Proverbs 3:8)* (6)
5 Pentecostal denomination, — of God (10)
6 One of the 'obvious' acts of the sinful nature *(Galatians 5:19, 21)* (4)
7 'I preached that they should repent and — to God' *(Acts 26:20)* (4)
10 ' — — , the world will not see me any more, but you will see me' *(John 14:19)* (6,4)
12 He betrayed Jesus: Judas — *(Luke 6:16)* (8)
13 Jesus to Peter: ' — — of my sheep' *(John 21:16)* (4,4)
16 The centurion said, 'Surely this man was — — of God' *(Mark 15:39)* (3,3)
18 Baked bread *(Mark 8:14)* (4)
19 'Blessing and honour, glory and power, be — Him' (Handel's *Messiah*) (4)

No 29

Across

8 'He poured out his life unto death, and was numbered with the —' *(Isaiah 53:12)* (13)

9 'When they had sung a hymn, they went — to the Mount of Olives *(Matthew 26:30)* (3)

10 Comes between Galatians and Philippians (9)

11 'Your heart will — and swell with joy' *(Isaiah 60:5)* (5)

13 Muslim holy month (7)

16 Ten ears (anag.) (7)

19 Under (poetic abbrev.) (5)

22 How Abram described himself to God when he complained that his inheritance would pass to a servant *(Genesis 15:2)* (9)

24 'Go to the — , you sluggard' *(Proverbs 6:6)* (3)

25 Debar from receiving Communion (13)

Down

1 *My — for His Highest* (Oswald Chambers' best-known book) (6)

2 Festival of the resurrection (6)

3 'His sons will prepare for war and — a great army' *(Daniel 11:10)* (8)

4 'Let not the — string his bow' *(Jeremiah 51:3)* (6)

5 Name of the River Thames in and around Oxford (4)

6 'From then on Judas watched for an opportunity — — him over' *(Matthew 26:16)* (2,4)

7 'But Christ is faithful — — — over God's house' *(Hebrews 3:6)* (2,1,3)

12 Long-handled implement used to till the soil *(Isaiah 7:25)* (3)

14 Order to which monks and nuns devote themselves (8)

15 Appropriate *(Proverbs 15:23)* (3)

16 I, uncle (anag.) (6)

17 'They gave him — — of broiled fish' *(Luke 24:42)* (1,5)

18 'Weren't there three men that we — — and threw into the fire?' *(Daniel 3:24)* (4,2)

20 Mountain where Noah's ark came to rest *(Genesis 8:4)* (6)

21 'Don't you know that friendship with the world is — towards God?' *(James 4:4)* (6)

23 Prominent architectural feature of large cathedrals such as St Paul's (4)

No 30

Across

1 One who owes money, goods or services *(Isaiah 24:2)* (6)

4 'A good measure, pressed down, — together and running over' *(Luke 6:38)* (6)

7 Continuous dull pain *(Proverbs 14:13)* (4)

8 This bread contains yeast *(Amos 4:5)* (8)

9 'But take heart! I have — the world' *(John 16:33)* (8)

13 And the rest (abbrev.) (3)

16 What Paul was accused of by Tertullus, the high priest's lawyer, in his trial before Felix *(Acts 24:5)* (13)

17 Rap (anag.) (3)

19 Founder of the Jesuits in 1534 (8)

24 'For where your — is, there your heart will be also' *(Luke 12:34)* (8)

25 The first word written on the wall during King Belshazzar's great banquet *(Daniel 5:25)* (4)
26 'We all, like sheep, have gone — ' *(Isaiah 53:6)* (6)
27 One was given in honour of Jesus in Bethany *(John 12:2)* (6)

Down

1 'The blind receive sight, the lame walk, the — hear, the dead are raised' *(Luke 7:22)* (4)
2 Conduct *(Colossians 1:21)* (9)
3 In the Catholic and Orthodox traditions, the body of a saint or his belongings, venerated as holy (5)
4 'Like a — of locusts men pounce on it' *(Isaiah 33:4)* (5)
5 Very old *(Genesis 44:20)* (4)
6 In Calvinist theology, one who is predestined by God to receive salvation (5)
10 How Nicodemus addressed Jesus when he visited him one night *(John 3:2)* (5)
11 Sea *(Psalm 148:7)* (5)
12 'I will — you, my God the King; I will praise your name for ever and ever' *(Psalm 145:1)* (5)
13 One of the groups of philosophers that Paul met in Athens, who disagreed with his teaching about the resurrection *(Acts 17:18)* (9)
14 Barred enclosure *(Ezekiel 19:9)* (4)
15 'Since we live by the Spirit, let us keep in — with the Spirit' *(Galatians 5:25)* (4)
18 Cares (anag.) (5)
20 Garish *(Ezekiel 16:16)* (5)
21 'So God said to Noah, "I am going to put — — to all people"' *(Genesis 6:13)* (2,3)
22 Just *(2 Corinthians 6:13)* (4)
23 'The — of the Lord is the beginning of knowledge' *(Proverbs 1:7)* (4)

No 31

Across

1 Military tactic used by Joshua to attack and destroy the city of Ai *(Joshua 8:2)* (6)

4 Place of learning (6)

8 'When Moses' hands grew — , they took a stone and put it under him and he sat on it' *(Exodus 17:12)* (5)

9 Unpleasant auguries of the end of the age, as forecast by Jesus *(Matthew 24:7)* (7)

10 Stronghold to which girls in King Xerxes' harem (including Esther) were taken *(Esther 2:8)* (7)

11 Where Saul went to consult a medium before fighting the Philistines *(1 Samuel 28:7)* (5)

12 Propitiation *(Hebrews 2:17)* (9)

17 Turn away *(Jeremiah 11:15)* (5)
19 So clear (anag.) (7)
21 'I have just got — , so I can't come': one excuse to be absent from the great banquet *(Luke 14:20)* (7)
22 Long weapon with a pointed head used by horsemen *(Job 39:23)* (5)
23 Musical beat (6)
24 What the Israelites were told to use to daub blood on their door-frames at the first Passover *(Exodus 12:22)* (6)

Down

1 Fasten *(Exodus 28:37)* (6)
2 Art bite (anag.) (7)
3 'The people of the city were divided; some — with the Jews, others with the apostles' *(Acts 14:4)* (5)
5 Contend *(Jeremiah 12:5)* (7)
6 Possessed *(Job 1:3)* (5)
7 Sheen *(Lamentations 4:1)* (6)
9 'You love evil rather than good, — rather than speaking the truth' *(Psalm 52:3)* (9)
13 Large flightless bird *(Job 39:13)* (7)
14 They were worth several hundred pounds each *(Matthew 25:15)* (7)
15 'A — went out to sow his seed' *(Matthew 13:3)* (6)
16 How Jesus described Jairus's daughter when he went into the room where she lay *(Mark 5:39)* (6)
18 The part of the day when the women went to the tomb on the first Easter morning *(John 20:1)* (5)
20 Narrow passageway between buildings *(Luke 14:21)* (5)

No 32

Across

1 Sent out three times on a reconnaissance mission from Noah's ark *(Genesis 8:8–12)* (4)

3 'The vilest — who truly believes, that moment from Jesus a pardon receives' (8)

9 Described by the 19th-century MP Sir Wilfred Lawson as 'the Devil in solution' (7)

10 'Whoever — his life for my sake will find it' *(Matthew 10:39)* (5)

11 King of Gezer *(Joshua 10:33)* (5)

12 Gideon's home town *(Judges 6:11)* (6)

14 The area under the jurisdiction of a primate, for example, Canterbury, York (13)

17 To him God promised that David would be king *(1 Chronicles 11:3)* (6)
19 A descendant of Aaron who was not allowed to offer food to God *(Leviticus 21:20)* (5)
22 'If any of you — wisdom, he should ask God' *(James 1:5)* (5)
23 I gain me (anag.) (7)
24 Relating to the armed forces *(1 Chronicles 5:18)* (8)
25 Title given to 2 Down (abbrev.) (4)

Down

1 Greek coins *(Acts 19:19)* (8)
2 Church of England incumbent (5)
4 What Epaphroditus was to Paul *(Philippians 2:25)* (6-7)
5 Mother of David's sixth son *(2 Samuel 3:5)* (5)
6 'We are hard pressed on every side, but not crushed; perplexed, but not in — ' *(2 Corinthians 4:8)* (7)
7 It destroys treasures on earth *(Matthew 6:19)* (4)
8 It threatened Paul in Jerusalem *(Acts 21:35)* (3,3)
13 Well-known Reference Bible that espoused dispensationalism (8)
15 Where the choir sits in a parish church (7)
16 Real do (anag.) (6)
18 'Martha, Martha… you are worried and — about many things' *(Luke 10:41)* (5)
20 'One man considers one day more sacred than another; another man considers every day — ' *(Romans 14:5)* (5)
21 A place with twelve springs and 70 palm trees where the Israelites camped *(Exodus 15:27)* (4)

No 33

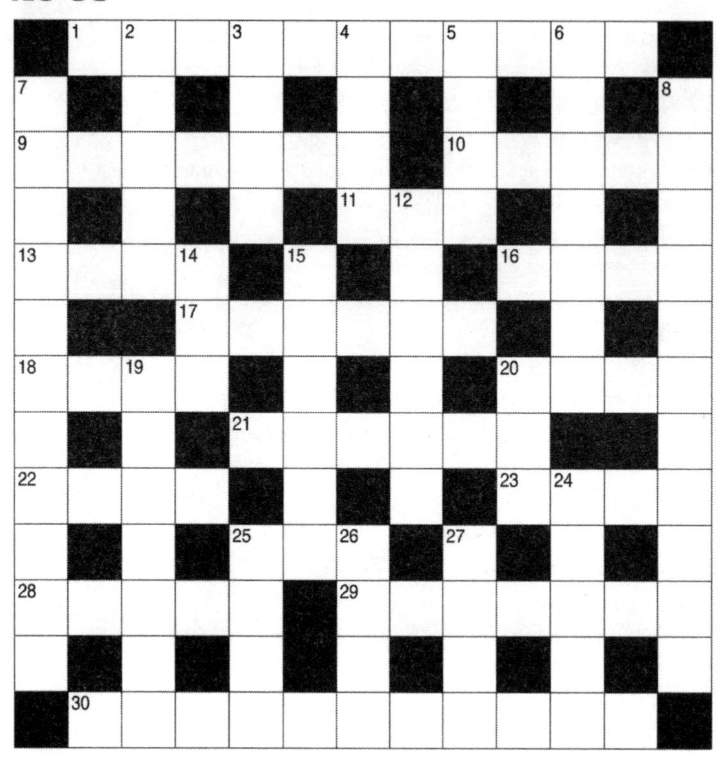

Across

1 In David's battle with the Arameans, 700 of these were killed *(2 Samuel 10:18)* (11)

9 'No — , impure or greedy person has any inheritance in the kingdom of God' *(Ephesians 5:5)* (7)

10 City on the banks of the River Nile (5)

11 Stamped addressed envelope (1,1,1)

13 Taverns (4)

16 'Be on your guard; stand — in the faith' *(1 Corinthians 16:13)* (4)

17 'He will not always — , nor will he harbour his anger for ever' *(Psalm 103:9)* (6)

18 and **27 Down** Where the magi came from and what guided them *(Matthew 2:1–2)* (4,4)

20 Ancient Celtic alphabet of 20 characters (4)
21 She married Esau when he was 40 years old *(Genesis 26:34)* (6)
22 A great-grandson of Noah *(Genesis 10:7)* (4)
23 Title accorded to certain Roman Catholic clerics (abbrev.) (4)
25 'My house will be a house of prayer; but you have made it a — of robbers' *(Luke 19:46)* (3)
28 Annie (anag.) (5)
29 Plead with *(Zechariah 7:2)* (7)
30 Tenth foundation of the new Jerusalem *(Revelation 21:20)* (11)

Down

2 'We have a building from God, an eternal house in heaven, not built by — hands' *(2 Corinthians 5:1)* (5)
3 Uncommon excellence *(Proverbs 20:15)* (4)
4 'You have exalted my horn like that of a wild ox; fine — have been poured upon me' *(Psalm 92:10)* (4)
5 — *Homo* ('Behold the Man') (4)
6 'He has given proof of this to all men by — him from the dead' *(Acts 17:31)* (7)
7 'Our — is in heaven' *(Philippians 3:20)* (11)
8 'This is a day you are to — ' *(Exodus 12:14)* (11)
12 Assault *(Psalm 17:9)* (6)
14 'Jesus found a young donkey and — upon it' *(John 12:14)* (3)
15 Liverpool dialect (6)
19 'Remember the — day by keeping it holy' *(Exodus 20:8)* (7)
20 Nineteenth-century German physicist after whom the unit of electrical resistance is named (3)
24 Nazirites were not allowed to eat this part of a grape *(Numbers 6:4)* (5)
25 'If anyone would come after me, he must — himself and take up his cross and follow me' *(Mark 8:34)* (4)
26 Evil Roman emperor from AD54 to 68, responsible for condemning hundreds of Christians to cruel deaths (4)
27 See 18 Across

No 34

Across

1 'You are no longer — and aliens, but fellow-citizens with God's people' *(Ephesians 2:19)* (10)

7 'Religion that God our Father — as pure and faultless is this' *(James 1:27)* (7)

8 'Do you want a — ? Signal then to Jesus' (5)

10 Throw *(Exodus 9:8)* (4)

11 We rank it (anag.) (8)

13 Encourage *(Isaiah 59:13)* (6)

15 'Then Jesus — from Galilee — the Jordan to be baptized by John' *(Matthew 3:13)* (4,2)

17 Coming to rest *(Matthew 3:16)* (8)

18 Provisional decree in divorce proceedings (4)

21 Long earnestly *(Psalm 84:2)* (5)
22 'Put these old rags and — clothes under your arms to pad the ropes' *(Jeremiah 38:12)* (4-3)
23 'He defends the cause of the — and the widow, and loves the alien' *(Deuteronomy 10:18)* (10)

Down

1 Self-evident truths *(Acts 19:36)* (5)
2 'Open your eyes and look at the fields! They are — for harvest' *(John 4:35)* (4)
3 'Your great learning is driving you — ' *(Acts 26:24)* (6)
4 'Spring of water' on the borders of Judah and Benjamin *(Joshua 15:9)* (8)
5 Rile Eve (anag.) (7)
6 'Remember, O Lord, how I have walked before you — and with wholehearted devotion' *(Isaiah 38:3)* (10)
9 Paul was mistakenly suspected of leading 4000 of these into the desert *(Acts 21:38)* (10)
12 Relationship of an omer to an ephah *(Exodus 16:36)* (3,5)
14 Galilean home town of Mary, 'from whom seven demons had come out' *(Luke 8:2)* (7)
16 'If I tell you, you will not believe me, and if I asked you, you would not — ' *(Luke 22:67–68)* (6)
19 Fetters *(Mark 5:4)* (5)
20 'No good — bears bad fruit' *(Luke 6:43)* (4)

No 35

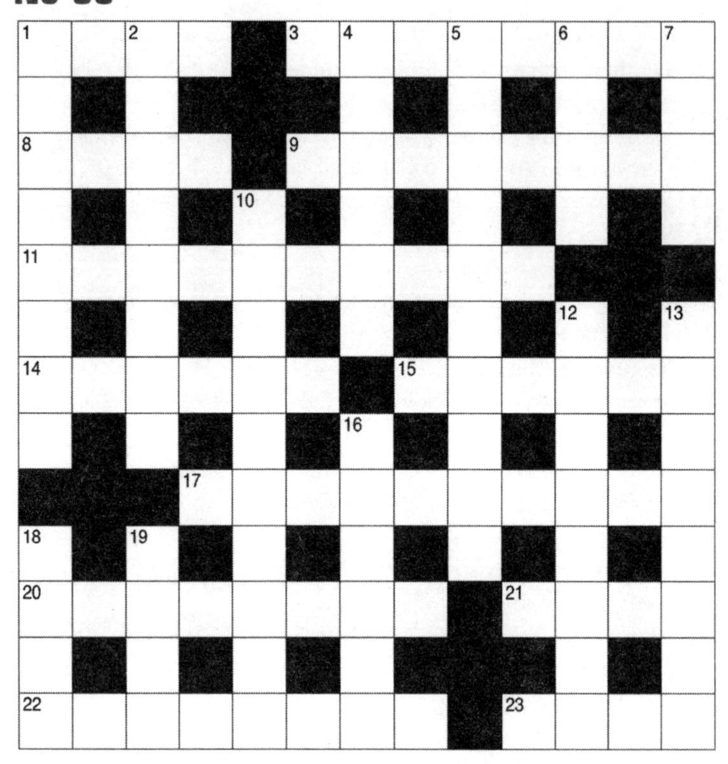

Across

1 Grandson of Mered and his Judean wife *(1 Chronicles 4:18)* (4)

3 He said of Jesus, 'This man has done nothing wrong' *(Luke 23:40–41)* (8)

8 Herb with pleasantly scented roots, present in the Beloved's orchard *(Song of Songs 4:13)* (4)

9 What God brought Sarah with the birth of Isaac *(Genesis 21:6)* (8)

11 Port on the Red Sea where King Solomon built ships *(1 Kings 9:26)* (5,5)

14 Donald — , Archbishop of Canterbury 1974–80 (6)

15 Cereal *(Ezekiel 4:9)* (6)

17 Jesus' description of a Pharisee *(Matthew 23:24)* (5,5)

20 Not as widely used at church services nowadays as used to be the case (8)

21 ' — all your anxiety on him because he cares for you' *(1 Peter 5:7)* (4)

22 One of the three strands of Methodism united in 1932 (8)

23 'They broke bread in their homes and ate together with — and sincere hearts' *(Acts 2:46)* (4)

Down

1 The rebuke of 3 Across, 'Don't you fear God... since you are under the same — ?' *(Luke 23:40)* (8)

2 Horse-drawn vehicle used by King Solomon *(Song of Songs 3:9)* (8)

4 Dearer (anag.) (6)

5 One-time editor of *Punch* and controversial writer and broadcaster who became a noted Christian, Malcolm — (10)

6 'When you sit to dine with a ruler, — well what is before you' *(Proverbs 23:1)* (4)

7 'God has made this Jesus, whom you crucified, both — and Christ' *(Acts 2:36)* (4)

10 One description of the inspired nature of scripture (10)

12 'The Son himself will be made subject to him who put everything under him, so that God may be — — — ' *(1 Corinthians 15:28)* (3,2,3)

13 Recognized as valid *(1 Samuel 3:20)* (8)

16 A long A (anag.) (6)

18 'For God does not — favouritism' *(Romans 2:11)* (4)

19 Comes between Joel and Obadiah (4)

No 36

Across

8 'Thanks be to God for his — gift' *(2 Corinthians 9:15)* (13)

9 The number of spies Joshua sent secretly to Jericho *(Joshua 2:1)* (3)

10 'The Lord detests — — , but he delights in men who are truthful' *(Proverbs 12:22)* (5,4)

11 Boredom (5)

13 ' — love has no one than this, that he lay down his life for his friends' *(John 15:13)* (7)

16 'How long must I — with my thoughts and every day have sorrow in my heart?' *(Psalm 13:2)* (7)

19 'He is the — of the invisible God, the first-born over all creation' *(Colossians 1:15)* (5)

22 Minimalist male clothing *(Job 12:18)* (9)

24 Drain *(Lamentations 2:12)* (3)
25 On purpose *(Exodus 21:13)* (13)

Down

1 'Jesus reached out his hand and caught him. "You of — faith," he said, "why did you doubt?"' *(Matthew 14:31)* (6)
2 Abut (6)
3 For example, David (8)
4 'But Mary stood outside the tomb — ' *(John 20:11)* (6)
5 'He rolled — — stone in front of the entrance to the tomb' *(Matthew 27:60)* (1,3)
6 Is boot (anag.) (6)
7 Thurible *(Leviticus 16:12)* (6)
12 'Neither death — life... will be able to separate us from the love of God' *(Romans 8:38–39)* (3)
14 Festival (January 6) marking the coming of the magi to the infant Christ (8)
15 'Which of you fathers, if your son... asks for an — , will give him a scorpion?' *(Luke 11:11–12)* (3)
16 Archaic word for 'heavens' or 'sky' used by Charles Wesley in the original version of 'Hark! the herald angels sing': 'Hark! how all the — rings' (6)
17 How the writer to the Hebrews described God: 'for whom and through whom everything — ' *(Hebrews 2:10)* (6)
18 'I plead with — and I plead with Syntyche to agree with each other in the Lord' *(Philippians 4:2)* (6)
20 Ancient *(Isaiah 58:12)* (3-3)
21 By Rome (anag.) (6)
23 Where Nathanael came from *(John 21:2)* (4)

No 37

Across

1 Rely *(Psalm 62:7)* (6)

4 'He stretches out the heavens like a — , and spreads them out like a tent to live in' *(Isaiah 40:22)* (6)

7 What the dove carried the olive leaf in, when it returned to Noah's ark *(Genesis 8:11)* (4)

8 Annoy *(1 Samuel 1:6)* (8)

9 Judah's last king, who ended his days as a blind prisoner in Babylon *(Jeremiah 52:11)* (8)

13 'They all — and were satisfied' *(Luke 9:17)* (3)

16 Eliphaz the Temanite was one; so was Bildad the Shuhite and Zophar the Naamathite *(Job 2:11; 16:2)* (4,9)

17 National Association of Evangelicals (of the USA) (1,1,1)

19 Popular song for New Year's Eve, Auld — — (4,4)
24 Able dock (anag.) (8)
25 The number of stones David chose for his confrontation with Goliath *(1 Samuel 17:40)* (4)
26 Elgar's best-known 'Variations' (6)
27 Soak *(Isaiah 16:9)* (6)

Down

1 Money owing *(Deuteronomy 15:3)* (4)
2 Conciliatory *(Titus 3:2)* (9)
3 'Do this, whenever you — it, in remembrance of me' *(1 Corinthians 11:25)* (5)
4 A group assisting in the governance of the Roman Catholic Church (5)
5 One of the gifts Joseph's brothers took with them on their second journey to Egypt *(Genesis 43:11)* (4)
6 'Reach out your hand and — — into my side. Stop doubting and believe' *(John 20:27)* (3,2)
10 Be outstandingly good *(2 Corinthians 8:7)* (5)
11 'What — — that you are mindful of him, the son of man that you care for him?' *(Psalm 8:4)* (2,3)
12 Horse's feet *(Judges 5:22)* (5)
13 Notice *(Deuteronomy 17:4)* (9)
14 Comes between 2 Chronicles and Nehemiah (4)
15 One of Israel's northern towns conquered by Ben-Hadad *(1 Kings 15:20)* (4)
18 Narnia's Lion (5)
20 One of the two rivers in which Naaman would have preferred to wash *(2 Kings 5:12)* (5)
21 Avarice—one of the evils that come from inside people *(Mark 7:22)* (5)
22 Knight Grand Cross of St Michael and St George (1,1,1,1)
23 Jacob's first wife *(Genesis 29:23)* (4)

No 38

Across

1 Protective covering recommended to the Ephesians *(Ephesians 6:11)* (6)

4 The number of apostles *(Matthew 10:2)* (6)

8 Tenth-century Bishop of Augsberg for 48 years, who became the first saint to be canonized by a pope (5)

9 'Do not — what is evil but what is good' *(3 John 11)* (7)

10 Reading desk in a church (7)

11 'He looked up and said, "I see people; they look like — walking around"' *(Mark 8:24)* (5)

12 One of the qualities that Paul exhorted Timothy to pursue *(1 Timothy 6:11)* (9)

17 One of the meaningless pleasures acquired by the Teacher *(Ecclesiastes 2:8)* (5)

19 'Like — babies, crave pure spiritual milk, so that by it you may grow up in your salvation' *(1 Peter 2:2)* (7)

21 Jesus said that Moses allowed this only because men's hearts were hard *(Matthew 19:8)* (7)

22 Girl's name (5)

23 Most sagacious *(Judges 5:29)* (6)

24 How Stephen, the first Christian martyr, died: after being — *(Acts 7:59)* (6)

Down

1 A Jew whom Paul met in Corinth, whose wife was Priscilla *(Acts 18:2)* (6)

2 For example, turning water into wine, feeding the five thousand, walking on water *(John 7:21)* (7)

3 Abram's relationship to Lot *(Genesis 14:12)* (5)

5 'Jesus answered, "It is —: 'Man does not live by bread alone.'"' *(Matthew 4:4)* (7)

6 'Peace I — with you; my peace I give you' *(John 14:27)* (5)

7 'May the Lord deal with me, be it — — severely, if anything but death separates you and me' *(Ruth 1:17)* (4,2)

9 Lack of knowledge *(Acts 17:30)* (9)

13 This woman 'followed Paul and believed' after his words to the Areopagus in Athens *(Acts 17:34)* (7)

14 Or noise (anag.) (7)

15 'Even though I walk through the valley of the — of death, I will fear no evil' *(Psalm 23:4)* (6)

16 ' — Christian soldiers, marching as to war' (6)

18 Saver (anag.) (5)

20 'Unless a grain of — falls to the ground and dies, it remains only a single seed' *(John 12:24)* (5)

No 39

Across

1 Salary *(Isaiah 19:10)* (4)

3 Question Jesus asked of those healed of leprosy, 'Were not all ten — ?' *(Luke 17:17)* (8)

9 Wide, elevated level area of land *(Joshua 13:9)* (7)

10 'So you also must be — , because the Son of Man will come… when you do not expect him' *(Matthew 24:44)* (5)

11 '[He] said to the man, "Stretch out your hand." He — — , and his hand was completely restored' *(Luke 6:10)* (3,2)

12 'Who has gathered up the wind in the — of his hand?' *(Proverbs 30:4)* (6)

14 Not born again (13)

17 'Again and again he — the same sacrifices, which can never take away sins' *(Hebrews 10:11)* (6)

19 Mails (anag.) (5)

22 'He — — here; he has risen' *(Matthew 28:6)* (2,3)

23 Defeated *(Judges 20:43)* (7)

24 Soldiers' quarters *(Acts 21:34)* (8)

25 'Pillars of marble' were how the Beloved described those of her Lover *(Song of Songs 5:15)* (4)

Down

1 Totally destroyed *(Genesis 7:23)* (5,3)

2 What the Philippian jailer was told to do with his prisoners Paul and Silas *(Acts 16:23)* (5)

4 Object of ridicule *(Job 12:4)* (8-5)

5 In most years, the month in which Easter falls (5)

6 For example, Caesarea, Joppa, Tyre, Sidon (7)

7 '[Jesus] was in the desert for forty — , being tempted by Satan' *(Mark 1:13)* (4)

8 'Hallelujah! Salvation and glory and power — to our God' *(Revelation 19:1)* (6)

13 Mend dots (anag.) (8)

15 Purifier *(Malachi 3:3)* (7)

16 Attacked *(1 Samuel 27:8)* (6)

18 The good Samaritan to the innkeeper: 'When I return, I will reimburse you for any — expense you may have' *(Luke 10:35)* (5)

20 How Matthew described the crowds who followed Jesus *(Matthew 4:25)* (5)

21 For example, one of 25 Across *(Judges 19:29)* (4)

No 40

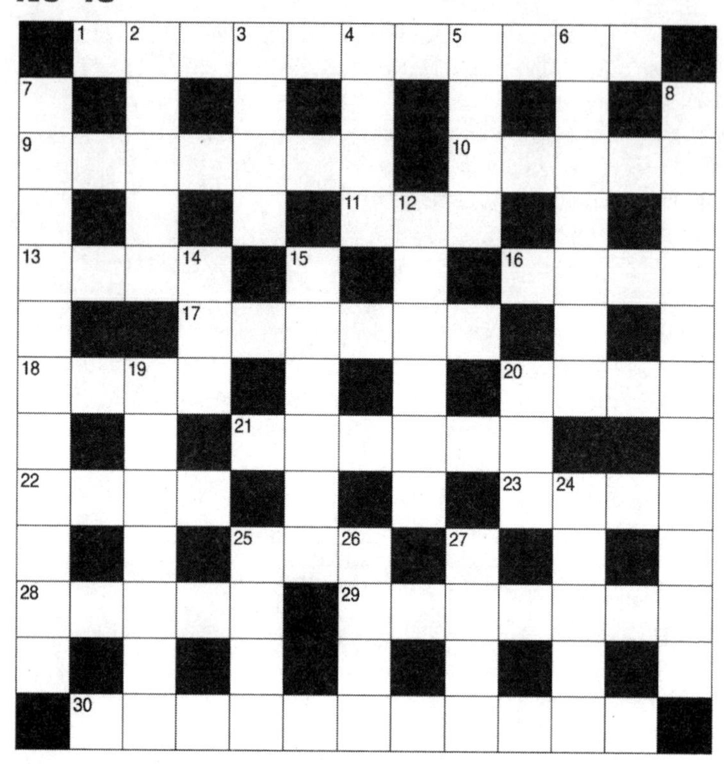

Across

1 These letters come between Romans and Galatians (11)
9 'You will not — me to the grave' *(Psalm 16:10)* (7)
10 King of Moab to whom the Israelites were subject for 18 years *(Judges 3:14)* (5)
11 Town possessing mineral spring (3)
13 Mede (anag.) (4)
16 High-fidelity (abbrev.) (4)
17 He succeeded his father Rehoboam as king of Judah *(1 Kings 14:31)* (6)
18 A son of Simeon *(Genesis 46:10)* (4)
20 Controversial religious book of the 1970s, *The — of God Incarnate* (4)

21 'He has received from the Father the promised Holy Spirit and has poured out what you — — and hear' *(Acts 2:33)* (3,3)
22 'You — me together in my mother's womb' *(Psalm 139:13)* (4)
23 Edit (anag.) (4)
25 'Who has believed our message and to whom has the — of the Lord been revealed?' *(Isaiah 53:1)* (3)
28 Abraham's brother *(Genesis 22:23)* (5)
29 'When Mordecai learned of — that had been — , he tore his clothes' *(Esther 4:1)* (3,4)
30 Sympathetic *(Proverbs 11:16)* (4-7)

Down

2 'That was why his parents said, "He is — —; ask him"' *(John 9:23)* (2,3)
3 Integrated Services Digital Network (1,1,1,1)
4 'Saul has slain his thousands, and David his — of thousands' *(1 Samuel 18:7)* (4)
5 Concept *(John 8:14)* (4)
6 'Do we, then, — the law by this faith? Not at all! Rather, we uphold the law' *(Romans 3:31)* (7)
7 Industrious *(2 Timothy 2:6)* (11)
8 'I pray also that the eyes of your heart may be — in order that you may know the hope to which he has called you *(Ephesians 1:18)* (11)
12 'Out of the same mouth come — and cursing' *(James 3:10)* (6)
14 This was how many of the Jewish leaders described Jesus *(John 10:20)* (3)
15 Vitality *(Job 20:11)* (6)
19 He urged David to kill Saul at Hakilah *(1 Samuel 26:8)* (7)
20 'So for a whole year Barnabas and Saul — with the church and taught great numbers of people' *(Acts 11:26)* (3)
24 'Hear, O Israel: The Lord our God, the Lord — — ' *(Deuteronomy 6:4)* (2,3)
25 Parched *(Matthew 12:43)* (4)
26 'In the image of God he created him; — and female he created them' *(Genesis 1:27)* (4)
27 Disparagement *(Psalm 15:3)* (4)

No 41

Across

1 'You are a chosen people, a royal — ' *(1 Peter 2:9)* (10)

7 Exact copy *(Joshua 22:28)* (7)

8 Jesus' first words to Jairus's daughter, 'My child, — — ' *(Luke 8:54)* (3,2)

10 Idol made by the Israelites while Moses was on Mount Sinai *(Exodus 32:4)* (4)

11 Role allotted to Joseph in Egypt *(Genesis 42:6)* (8)

13 'Lord, when did we — — hungry and feed you?' *(Matthew 25:37)* (3,3)

15 'Though seeing, they do — —; though hearing, they do not hear or understand' *(Matthew 13:13)* (3,3)

17 Happening *(1 Kings 21:1)* (8)

18 'Whatever was to my profit I now consider loss for the — of Christ' *(Philippians 3:7)* (4)

21 National Society for the Prevention of Cruelty to Children (1,1,1,1,1)

22 Stamp on *(Amos 2:7)* (7)

23 Liable to rot *(1 Corinthians 15:42)* (10)

Down

1 Of the pope (5)

2 'The earth is the Lord's, and everything — — ' *(Psalm 24:1)* (2,2)

3 Hebrew word for the kind of peace that Jesus promised (6)

4 Member of a 16th-century Protestant reform movement in France (8)

5 Sing out (anag.) (7)

6 Ceremonial column of people on the move *(1 Samuel 10:5)* (10)

9 One of the things love always does *(1 Corinthians 13:7)* (10)

12 Esther's cousin who foiled a plot to assassinate King Xerxes *(Esther 2:7, 22)* (8)

14 See cape (anag.) (7)

16 'No one can — them out of my hand' *(John 10:28)* (6)

19 Often mistakenly identified as the fruit that led to the first sin *(Joel 1:12)* (5)

20 'He was led like a — to the slaughter' *(Isaiah 53:7)* (4)

No 42

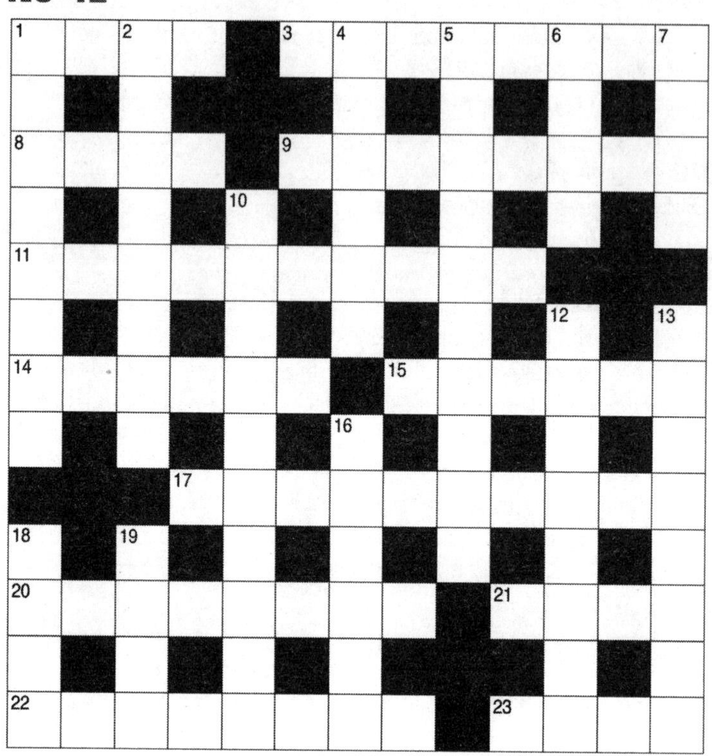

Across

1 Infant *(Luke 2:12)* (4)

3 Luis must (anag.) (8)

8 What Jesus called the devil *(John 8:44)* (4)

9 'My God, my God, why have you — me?' *(Matthew 27:46)* (8)

11 Anglican form of church government (10)

14 'Those who hope in the Lord will renew their strength. They will soar on wings like — ' *(Isaiah 40:31)* (6)

15 Ministers of religion (6)

17 Make stronger *(1 Thessalonians 3:13)* (10)

20 Devoutness *(1 Timothy 2:2)* (8)

21 The father of Jesse *(Ruth 4:22)* (4)

22 Pool where Jesus healed a man who had been an invalid for 38 years *(John 5:2)* (8)

23 '[Jesus] said to them, " — here and keep watch"' *(Mark 14:34)* (4)

Down

1 Follower of Christ *(Acts 16:1)* (8)

2 One of the punishments endured by Paul *(2 Corinthians 6:5)* (8)

4 Soldiers *(Exodus 14:9)* (6)

5 Scholarly study of melody, harmony and rhythm (10)

6 'I am God, and there is none — me' *(Isaiah 46:9)* (4)

7 'And how can they preach unless they are — ?' *(Romans 10:15)* (4)

10 Favourable reception *(1 Timothy 1:15)* (10)

12 Hip orbit (anag.) (8)

13 End of life *(Isaiah 22:14)* (5,3)

16 'About midnight the sailors — they were approaching land' *(Acts 27:27)* (6)

18 He married Jezebel *(1 Kings 16:30–31)* (4)

19 'According to your great compassion — out my transgressions' *(Psalm 51:1)* (4)

No 43

Across

8 Laban complained he had not been allowed to kiss them when Jacob fled with his family *(Genesis 31:28)* (13)

9 In favour of (3)

10 'The child's father and mother — at what was said about him' *(Luke 2:33)* (9)

11 Swagger *(Psalm 12:8)* (5)

13 'Terrors — him on every side and dog his every step' *(Job 18:11)* (7)

16 Bay bits (anag.) (7)

19 Preach, address an audience, speak in public (5)

22 Holy Communion (9)

24 'On their way to — out the land, Joshua instructed them, "Go and make a survey of the land"' *(Joshua 18:8)* (3)

25 Joseph advised Pharaoh to appoint these to administer his grain storage plan *(Genesis 41:34)* (13)

Down

1 'Assyria's pride will be brought down and — sceptre will pass away' *(Zechariah 10:11)* (6)

2 'And Jesus grew in wisdom and stature, and in — with God and men' *(Luke 2:52)* (6)

3 The descendants of Esau *(Genesis 36:9)* (8)

4 The components of the crown that Jesus was made to wear before his crucifixion *(John 19:2)* (6)

5 Colour of cloth which was to cover holy objects in the tabernacle when moving camp *(Numbers 4:6–12)* (4)

6 One of the gold articles plundered from the Midianites offered to the Lord by the Israelite army 'to make atonement' *(Numbers 31:50)* (6)

7 'The fathers have eaten sour grapes, and the children's teeth are set — — ' *(Jeremiah 31:29)* (2,4)

12 Ate (anag.) (3)

14 'We ourselves… groan inwardly as we wait eagerly for our — as sons' *(Romans 8:23)* (8)

15 Abram's nephew *(Genesis 14:12)* (3)

16 Rupture *(Job 30:14)* (6)

17 'Yet to all who received him… he gave the right to — children of God' *(John 1:12)* (6)

18 'I… asked him the true meaning of all — . — he told me and gave me the interpretation of these things' *(Daniel 7:16)* (4,2)

20 Military units *(Exodus 14:20)* (6)

21 'Joseph her husband was a righteous man and did not want to — her to public disgrace' *(Matthew 1:19)* (6)

23 Diva (anag.) (4)

No 44

Across

1 'I pray that out of his glorious — he may strengthen you with power through his Spirit in your inner being' *(Ephesians 3:16)* (6)

4 'Saul's father Kish and — father Ner were sons of Abiel' *(1 Samuel 14:51)* (6)

7 'Praise the Lord, O my — ' *(Psalm 103:1)* (4)

8 See 5 Down

9 Laws *(1 Kings 11:33)* (8)

13 'Who of you by worrying can — a single hour to his life?' *(Luke 12:25)* (3)

16 Artistry *(Exodus 31:5)* (13)

17 'Your young men will see visions, your — men will dream dreams' *(Acts 2:17)* (3)

19 How David described his Lord *(Psalm 19:14)* (8)

24 'If this city is built and its — — restored, you will be left with nothing in Trans-Euphrates' *(Ezra 4:16)* (5,3)

25 'The holy Scriptures, which are able to make you — for salvation through faith in Christ Jesus' *(2 Timothy 3:15)* (4)

26 Intended destination of arrows *(Lamentations 3:12)* (6)

27 Eve hit (anag.) (6)

Down

1 'For I am gentle and humble in heart, and you will find — for your souls' *(Matthew 11:29)* (4)

2 Where Peter was when he denied Christ three times *(Luke 22:55)* (9)

3 Remarkable early 20th-century Indian evangelist, a convert from Hinduism, — Sundar Singh (5)

4 'Now the king had put the officer on whose — — leaned in charge of the gate' *(2 Kings 7:17)* (3,2)

5 and **8 Across** The Lover describes this facial feature of the Beloved thus: 'Your — is like the tower of Lebanon looking towards — ' *(Song of Songs 7:4)* (4,8)

6 'Stand firm then, with the belt of truth buckled — your waist' *(Ephesians 6:14)* (5)

10 Trout (anag.) (5)

11 Easily frightened *(1 Thessalonians 5:14)* (5)

12 The ability to perceive *(Ecclesiastes 10:3)* (5)

13 One of the clans descended from Benjamin *(Numbers 26:38)* (9)

14 '"It is one of the Twelve," he replied, "one who — bread into the bowl with me"' *(Mark 14:20)* (4)

15 Resound *(Zephaniah 2:14)* (4)

18 Traditional seat of the Dalai Lama (5)

20 Precise *(John 4:53)* (5)

21 Build *(Ezekiel 4:2)* (5)

22 Beat harshly *(Acts 22:25)* (4)

23 Darius, who succeeded Belshazzar as king of the Babylonians, was one *(Daniel 5:31)* (4)

No 45

Across

1 'The people were — at his teaching' *(Mark 1:22)* (6)

4 'He saved —; let him save himself' *(Luke 23:35)* (6)

8 He addressed the crowd in Jerusalem on the day of Pentecost *(Acts 2:14)* (5)

9 Father of James and John *(Matthew 4:21)* (7)

10 One who charges another with an offence *(Job 31:35)* (7)

11 ' — thy ministers with righteousness' (Book of Common Prayer) (5)

12 and 15 Down 'All — is God-breathed and is — for teaching, rebuking, correcting and training in righteousness' *(2 Timothy 3:16)* (9,6)

17 'No — of the field had yet appeared on the earth and no plant of the field had yet sprung up' *(Genesis 2:5)* (5)

19 Made to feel embarrassed *(Isaiah 24:23)* (7)

21 This man built his house on sand *(Matthew 7:26)* (7)

22 David's hypocritical message to Joab on the death in battle of Uriah: 'Don't let this — you' *(2 Samuel 11:25)* (5)

23 Detest *(Job 10:1)* (6)

24 'God made two great lights, the greater light to govern the day and the — light to govern the night' *(Genesis 1:16)* (6)

Down

1 To make a serious request *(1 Corinthians 1:10)* (6)

2 Launches an assault against *(Genesis 32:8)* (7)

3 'The wicked man — deceptive wages' *(Proverbs 11:18)* (5)

5 Tuba ale (anag.) (7)

6 'The day thou gavest, Lord, is — ' (5)

7 Old Testament measure of weight, equivalent to about 12 grammes *(Exodus 30:13)* (6)

9 Where Elijah restored life to the son of a widow with whom he lodged *(1 Kings 17:10)* (9)

13 Paul said of whatever was to his profit, 'I consider them — , that I may gain Christ and be found in him' *(Philippians 3:8)* (7)

14 City visited by Paul, described by the city clerk as 'the guardian of the temple of the great Artemis' *(Acts 19:35)* (7)

15 See 12 Across

16 Rioted (anag.) (6)

18 She had a surprise when she answered the door and found 8 Across outside *(Acts 12:13)* (5)

20 Maltreat *(1 Chronicles 10:4)* (5)

No 46

Across

1 'A little later someone else saw Peter and said, "You — are one of them"' *(Luke 22:58)* (4)

3 Giving *(1 Peter 2:5)* (8)

9 They came to Jerusalem seeking an infant king *(Matthew 2:7)* (3,4)

10 'An athlete... does not receive the victor's crown unless he competes according to the — ' *(2 Timothy 2:5)* (5)

11 Pacifist, temperance advocate, open-air preacher, leading 20th-century Methodist, Donald — (5)

12 'Come quickly to — — , O Lord my Saviour' *(Psalm 38:22)* (4,2)

14 'The God of Abraham, — — — , the God of our fathers, has glorified his servant Jesus' *(Acts 3:13)* (5,3,5)

17 Sear by intense heat *(Revelation 16:8)* (6)

19 'It is better to take refuge in the Lord than to trust — —' *(Psalm 118:8)* (2,3)
22 Goods *(Nehemiah 13:15)* (5)
23 i.e. train (anag.) (7)
24 Surrounding area *(Luke 24:50)* (8)
25 'Righteousness will be his — and faithfulness the sash round his waist' *(Isaiah 11:5)* (4)

Down

1 Elegant and creative *(Exodus 31:4)* (8)
2 'Listen, I tell you a mystery: We will not all — , but we will all be changed' *(1 Corinthians 15:51)* (5)
4 'I... delight to see how orderly you are and how firm your — — — is' *(Colossians 2:5)* (5,2,6)
5 Enlist *(2 Samuel 24:2)* (5)
6 Of the Muslim faith (7)
7 Sharp intake of breath *(Job 11:20)* (4)
8 Woven cloth *(Ezekiel 16:13)* (6)
13 Plentiful *(Romans 5:17)* (8)
15 CIA char (anag.) (7)
16 Paul and Silas stopped him committing suicide after an earthquake in Philippi *(Acts 16:27–28)* (6)
18 One of the ingredients in the making of incense for the Lord *(Exodus 30:34)* (5)
20 Episcopal headwear (5)
21 Inhabitant of, say, Russia, Ukraine, Poland, Slovakia or Bulgaria (4)

No 47

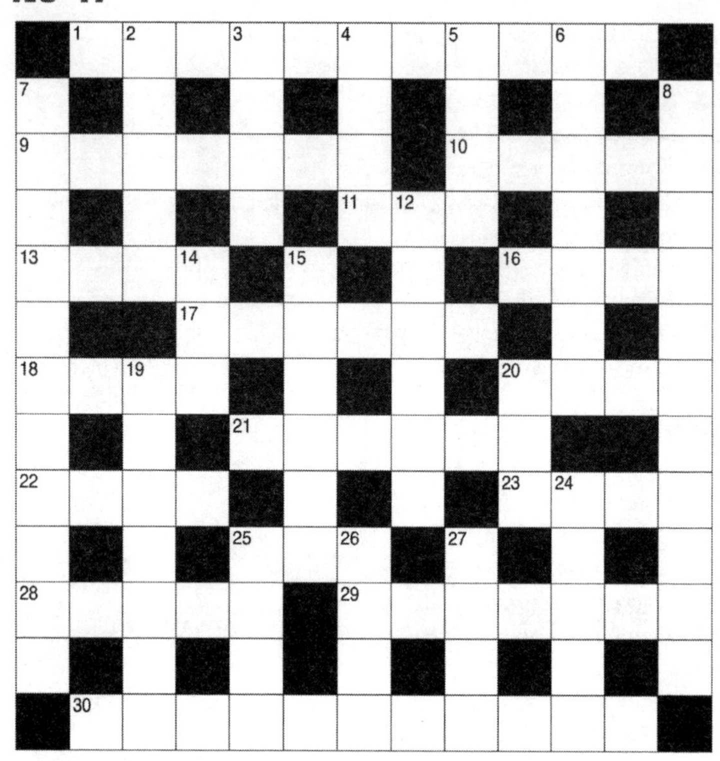

Across

1 The sixth disciple *(Matthew 10:3)* (11)

9 'And lead us not into temptation, but deliver us from the — — ' *(Matthew 6:13)* (4,3)

10 Love intensely *(Song of Songs 1:4)* (5)

11 From Mt Carmel to Jezreel, Elijah — all the way *(1 Kings 18:46)* (3)

13 One of the Midianite leaders who was captured and killed after Gideon's victory in the valley near Moreh *(Judges 7:25)* (4)

16 Metallic element (4)

17 At line (anag.) (6)

18 'Cursed is everyone who is — on a tree' *(Galatians 3:13)* (4)

20 Where Samson killed a thousand Philistines with a donkey's jawbone *(Judges 15:14)* (4)

21 He succeeded Moses *(Deuteronomy 34:9)* (6)
22 'When he saw him, he took — on him' *(Luke 10:33)* (4)
23 'For — is the gate and broad is the road that leads to destruction' *(Matthew 7:13)* (4)
25 'The god of this — has blinded the minds of unbelievers' *(2 Corinthians 4:4)* (3)
28 Fear or terror *(Psalm 31:22)* (5)
29 'We, who are many, are one body, for we all — of the one loaf' *(1 Corinthians 10:17)* (7)
30 Assyrian ruler assassinated by his sons while worshipping his god Nisroch *(2 Kings 19:37)* (11)

Down

2 'For as in Adam all die, so in Christ all will be made — ' *(1 Corinthians 15:22)* (5)
3 'After supper he — the cup' *(1 Corinthians 11:25)* (4)
4 The request of a man of Macedonia in Paul's vision: 'Come — to Macedonia and help us' *(Acts 16:9)* (4)
5 He disobeyed his father Judah by refusing to impregnate his dead brother's wife *(Genesis 38:9)* (4)
6 I veto me (anag.) (7)
7 Fourth king of Judah *(1 Kings 15:24)* (11)
8 Priest of God Most High, who blessed Abram *(Genesis 14:18)* (11)
12 'I have made you — — for the Gentiles' *(Acts 13:47)* (1,5)
14 Implore *(1 Samuel 15:25)* (3)
15 'Out of the eater, something to eat; out of the — , something sweet' *(Judges 14:14)* (6)
19 'I am the most ignorant of men; I do — — a man's understanding' *(Proverbs 30:2)* (3,4)
20 'Sin shall not be your master, because you are not under — , but under grace' *(Romans 6:14)* (3)
24 Native of, say, Baghdad (5)
25 The last word in the Bible *(Revelation 22:21)* (4)
26 Heroic tale (4)
27 'Then you will know the truth, and the truth will set you — ' *(John 8:32)* (4)

No 48

Across

1 He was replaced as king of Judah by his uncle Mattaniah *(2 Kings 24:17)* (10)

7 'Let us fix our eyes on Jesus… who for the joy set before him — the cross' *(Hebrews 12:2)* (7)

8 Relieved (5)

10 Impetuous *(Acts 19:36)* (4)

11 Surprised and alarmed *(Luke 24:37)* (8)

13 'It is — for a camel to go through the eye of a needle than for the rich to enter the kingdom of God' *(Mark 10:25)* (6)

15 Directions for the conduct of a church service (6)

17 One of the acts of the sinful nature *(Galatians 5:19)* (8)

18 and **20 Down** 'She began to wet his — with her tears. Then she wiped them with her — ' *(Luke 7:38)* (4,4)

21 'We will all be changed, in a flash, in the twinkling of an — , — the last trumpet' *(1 Corinthians 15:51–52)* (3,2)

22 'But he replied, "Lord, I am — — go with you to prison and to death"' *(Luke 22:33)* (5,2)

23 Third person of the Trinity *(2 Corinthians 13:14)* (4,6)

Down

1 He betrayed Jesus *(Matthew 27:3)* (5)

2 Paul's assurance to the Philippian jailer: 'Don't — yourself! We are all here!' *(Acts 16:28)* (4)

3 'Fear God and keep his commandments, for this — the whole — of man' *(Ecclesiastes 12:13)* (2,4)

4 The sort of giver God loves *(2 Corinthians 9:7)* (8)

5 Sun rail (anag.) (7)

6 Naboth, the ill-fated vineyard owner, was one *(1 Kings 21:1)* (10)

9 Paul said of young widows, 'When their sensual desires overcome their — to Christ, they want to marry' *(1 Timothy 5:11)* (10)

12 This was how Joseph of Arimathea practised his discipleship 'because he feared the Jews' *(John 19:38)* (8)

14 Mop ruse (anag.) (7)

16 Foment *(Philippians 1:17)* (4,2)

19 Where Joseph and Mary escaped to with the baby Jesus *(Matthew 2:14)* (5)

20 See 18 Across

No 49

Across

1 'The blind receive sight, the — walk' *(Luke 7:22)* (4)
3 Got *(Philippians 3:12)* (8)
8 Leave out *(Jeremiah 26:2)* (4)
9 Castigated for using dishonest scales *(Hosea 12:7)* (8)
11 Weighty *(1 John 5:3)* (10)
14 'Now the serpent was more — than any of the wild animals the Lord God had made' *(Genesis 3:1)* (6)
15 'Those controlled by the sinful nature cannot — God' *(Romans 8:8)* (6)
17 Because Israel lacked one of these, tools had to be sharpened by the Philistines *(1 Samuel 13:19)* (10)

20 In his vision of the two eagles and the vine, this is how Ezekiel described the latter *(Ezekiel 17:8)* (8)

21 Rite (anag.) (4)

22 Nine gigs (anag.) (8)

23 'The eye cannot say to the — , "I don't need you"' *(1 Corinthians 12:21)* (4)

Down

1 'Flee for your lives! Don't — — , and don't stop anywhere in the plain!' *(Genesis 19:17)* (4,4)

2 Principal thoroughfare *(Numbers 20:19)* (4,4)

4 'The tax collector… beat his — and said, "God have mercy on me, a sinner"' *(Luke 18:13)* (6)

5 'The zeal of the Lord Almighty will — this' *(2 Kings 19:31)* (10)

6 'The day of the Lord is — for all nations' *(Obadiah 15)* (4)

7 Specified day *(Acts 21:26)* (4)

10 Deadly epidemic *(Deuteronomy 32:24)* (10)

12 Roman Catholic church which has special ceremonial rights (8)

13 Tied up *(2 Kings 7:10)* (8)

16 In his speech to the Sanhedrin, Stephen described Moses as 'powerful in speech and — ' *(Acts 7:22)* (6)

18 'Although he did not remove the high places, — heart was fully committed to the Lord all his life' *(1 Kings 15:14)* (4)

19 Tribe *(Deuteronomy 29:18)* (4)

No 50

Across

8 How the Abyss (NIV) is described in the Authorized Version *(Revelation 9:1)* (10,3)

9 Frozen water *(Ezekiel 1:22)* (3)

10 The Ten Commandments (9)

11 In Roman Catholic theology, neither heaven nor hell (5)

13 Des cons (anag.) (7)

16 'Though [your sins] are red as — , they shall be like wool' *(Isaiah 1:18)* (7)

19 Keen *(Romans 1:15)* (5)

22 Repugnant, loathsome *(Jeremiah 24:9)* (9)

24 Drink like an animal *(Judges 7:5)* (3)

25 First and last *(Revelation 22:13)* (5,3,5)

Down

1 Father of Ahi, a Gadite *(1 Chronicles 5:15)* (6)

2 Where David found the stone with which he killed Goliath *(1 Samuel 17:40)* (6)

3 'Hour by hour fresh lips are making thy — doings heard on high' (8)

4 'And there were shepherds living out in the fields near by, keeping watch over their — at night' *(Luke 2:8)* (6)

5 United Society for Christian Literature (1,1,1,1)

6 'If he refuses to listen even to the church, treat him as you would — — or a tax collector' *(Matthew 18:17)* (1,5)

7 Where Paul was taken when things became difficult for him in Berea *(Acts 17:15)* (6)

12 Istituto per le Opere di Religione (Vatican Bank) (1,1,1)

14 'Therefore, if anyone is in Christ, he is a new — ; the old has gone, the new has come!' *(2 Corinthians 5:17)* (8)

15 Used to colour ram skins red for use in the tabernacle *(Exodus 25:5)* (3)

16 Vat car (anag.) (6)

17 'Be joyful — — , patient in affliction, faithful in prayer' *(Romans 12:12)* (6)

18 'The parts that are unpresentable are treated with special modesty, while our presentable parts — — special treatment' *(1 Corinthians 12:23)* (4,2)

20 Ancient rowing boat *(Isaiah 33:21)* (6)

21 Say again *(2 Corinthians 11:16)* (6)

23 What Jesus did in the synagogue in Nazareth after he stood up *(Luke 4:16)* (4)

No 51

Across

1 'If you love those who love you, what — is that to you?' *(Luke 6:32)* (6)

4 'They threw the ship's — overboard' *(Acts 27:19)* (6)

7 The first murderer *(Genesis 4:8)* (4)

8 He was the head Levite in charge of the singing when the ark of God was brought back to Jerusalem *(1 Chronicles 15:22)* (8)

9 Samson was noted for this *(Judges 16:6)* (8)

13 Solicit money or food from passers by *(Acts 3:2)* (3)

16 What William Booth's Christian Mission became in 1878 (9,4)

17 Alliance of Religions and Conservation (1,1,1)

19 'I will praise your name for ever and ever. — — I will praise you' *(Psalm 145:1–2)* (5,3)

24 Simon had (anag.) (8)
25 Desperate *(Deuteronomy 28:48)* (4)
26 Elisha witnessed the boy he was seeking to resuscitate do this seven times before opening his eyes *(2 Kings 4:35)* (6)
27 The belly and thighs of the statue in Nebuchadnezzar's dream were made of this *(Daniel 2:32)* (6)

Down

1 'Before the — crows, you will disown me three times' *(Matthew 26:75)* (4)
2 Relating to the books of the Bible between Acts and Revelation (9)
3 'They have — the Lord out of the tomb, and we don't know where they have put him!' *(John 20:2)* (5)
4 Belief (5)
5 'Take the following fine spices: ... 250 shekels of fragrant — ' *(Exodus 30:23)* (4)
6 'Do not — Jerusalem, but wait for the gift' *(Acts 1:4)* (5)
10 A seer (anag.) (5)
11 'Even there your hand will — me' *(Psalm 139:10)* (5)
12 The wild variety was part of John the Baptist's diet *(Mark 1:6)* (5)
13 A non-Greek speaker who was looked down on by civilized people *(Colossians 3:11)* (9)
14 Famous 1950s musical whose characters included members of 16 Across, — *and Dolls* (4)
15 The province from which Paul wrote to the Corinthians *(1 Corinthians 16:19)* (4)
18 'He was standing in the gateway with a linen cord and a measuring — — his hand' *(Ezekiel 40:3)* (3,2)
20 'Today, if you hear his — , do not harden your hearts as you did in the rebellion' *(Hebrews 3:15)* (5)
21 The Jericho prostitute who hid two Israelite spies on the roof of her house *(Hebrews 11:31)* (5)
22 'And now these three remain: faith, — and love. But the greatest of these is love' *(1 Corinthians 13:13)* (4)
23 'God has numbered the days of your reign and brought it to an end' *(Daniel 5:26)* (4)

No 52

Across

1 Arouse *(Song of Songs 2:7)* (6)

4 Extinguish *(Isaiah 1:31)* (6)

8 '"They — — ," you will say, "but I'm not hurt!"' *(Proverbs 23:35)* (3,2)

9 Unhappiness *(Nehemiah 2:2)* (7)

10 Jewish (7)

11 Dirge (anag.) (5)

12 'A truthful witness gives honest — , but a false witness tells lies' *(Proverbs 12:17)* (9)

17 Paul quoted from the second one in his address in the synagogue at Pisidian Antioch *(Acts 13:33)* (5)

19 'Do not use your freedom to — the sinful nature' *(Galatians 5:13)* (7)

21 'As you can see, he has done nothing to — death' *(Luke 23:15)* (7)

22 Name applied by Isaiah to Jerusalem *(Isaiah 29:1)* (5)

23 'All the people — — one man, saying, "None of us will go home"' *(Judges 20:8)* (4,2)

24 Lazarus, who was carried by angels to Abraham's side when he died, was one *(Luke 16:20)* (6)

Down

1 Appalled *(Job 26:11)* (6)

2 'In an — to escape from the ship, the sailors let the lifeboat down into the sea' *(Acts 27:30)* (7)

3 Expel *(Acts 18:16)* (5)

5 'But I have a baptism to — , and how distressed I am until it is completed!' *(Luke 12:50)* (7)

6 'Of the increase of his government and peace there will be — — ' *(Isaiah 9:7)* (2,3)

7 Hurry *(Psalm 119:60)* (6)

9 'For I desire mercy, not — , and acknowledgement of God rather than burnt offerings' *(Hosea 6:6)* (9)

13 One of its towns was Sychar, where Jesus met a woman at Jacob's well *(John 4:5)* (7)

14 Shouting *(Acts 7:57)* (7)

15 Arachnid *(Isaiah 59:5)* (6)

16 One of Paul's first converts in Philippi was Lydia, a — in purple cloth *(Acts 16:14)* (6)

18 Donkeys (5)

20 Raked (anag.) (5)

No 53

Across

1 'The baby in my — leaped for joy' *(Luke 1:44)* (4)

3 A 'don't know' in matters of faith (8)

9 In the distant past *(Jeremiah 2:20)* (4,3)

10 Armada *(1 Kings 10:22)* (5)

11 Where Moses was confronted with the burning bush *(Exodus 3:1)* (5)

12 Hair colour indicative of skin infection *(Leviticus 13:30)* (6)

14 'The worries of this life and the — of wealth choke it, making it unfruitful' *(Matthew 13:22)* (13)

17 Expel *(2 Kings 13:23)* (6)

19 What Jesus wrapped round his waist when he washed his disciples' feet *(John 13:4)* (5)

22 The sixth plague to afflict the Egyptians *(Exodus 9:9)* (5)
23 For nine (anag.) (7)
24 Where there is no time *(Psalm 93:2)* (8)
25 Goliath's challenge to the Israelite army in the Valley of Elah: 'This day I — the ranks of Israel!' *(1 Samuel 17:10)* (4)

Down

1 'I will become angry with them and forsake them; I — — my face from them' *(Deuteronomy 31:17)* (4,4)
2 Usual description of prophets such as Amos, Hosea, Micah, and so on (5)
4 'They cannot see the light of the gospel of the — — — , who is the image of God' *(2 Corinthians 4:4)* (5,2,6)
5 An animal's internal edible parts *(Leviticus 4:11)* (5)
6 Popular 20th-century religious novel by Lloyd C. Douglas, which became a 1953 film starring Richard Burton (3,4)
7 'A — on a hill cannot be hidden' *(Matthew 5:14)* (4)
8 One of the exiles, a descendant of Bebai, who married a foreign woman *(Ezra 10:28)* (6)
13 Old Testament hymn-singing (8)
15 'And O what transport of delight from thy pure — floweth' (7)
16 Of felt (anag.) (3,3)
18 'So — the — sets you free, you will be free indeed' *(John 8:36)* (2,3)
20 Comes between 'bad' and 'worst' *(John 5:14)* (5)
21 'Neither height nor depth… will be — to separate us from the love of God' *(Romans 8:39)* (4)

No 54

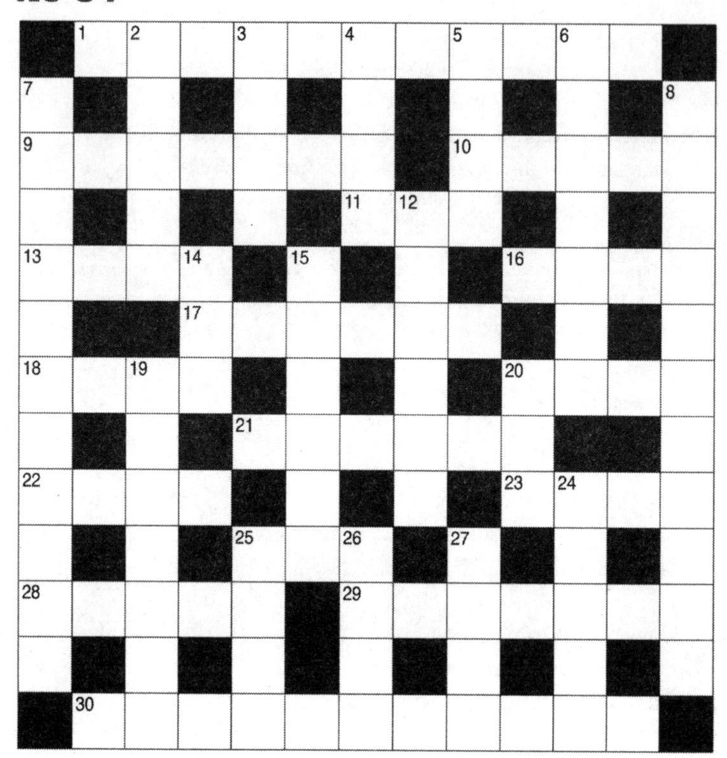

Across

1 Overpowered *(Deuteronomy 11:4)* (11)

9 'The — are mantled with corn' *(Psalm 65:13)* (7)

10 'Each man — a sword to his side' *(Exodus 32:27)* (5)

11 On the death of Jesus the curtain in the temple was torn from — to bottom *(Matthew 27:51)* (3)

13 Stagger *(Isaiah 28:7)* (4)

16 'Anyone, then, who knows the good he ought — — and doesn't do it, sins' *(James 4:17)* (2,2)

17 Stir up or provoke *(Acts 13:50)* (6)

18 Burden *(Luke 11:46)* (4)

20 'As far as the east is from the — , so far has he removed our transgressions from us' *(Psalm 103:12)* (4)

21 Sign *(Luke 23:38)* (6)
22 'After that, Jesus poured water into a basin and began to — his disciples' feet' *(John 13:5)* (4)
23 The nature of the seven ears of corn which swallowed up the good ears in Pharaoh's dream *(Genesis 41:23)* (4)
25 Has (anag.) (3)
28 'This is the account of Shem, Ham and Japheth, — sons' *(Genesis 10:1)* (5)
29 'I will… make them drunk, so that they… sleep for — and — awake' *(Jeremiah 51:39)* (4,3)
30 Paul said of him, 'he often refreshes me and is not ashamed of my chains' *(2 Timothy 1:16)* (11)

Down

2 Worth *(Matthew 13:46)* (5)
3 'A bruised — he will not break' *(Matthew 12:20)* (4)
4 'Suddenly a great company of the heavenly — appeared with the angel' *(Luke 2:13)* (4)
5 Slip (anag.) (4)
6 'Take an awl and push it through his — — into the door, and he will become your servant for life' *(Deuteronomy 15:17)* (3,4)
7 Bountiful *(2 Corinthians 8:2)* (11)
8 'Therefore, as we have — , let us do good to all people' *(Galatians 6:10)* (11)
12 Acquire *(2 Timothy 2:10)* (6)
14 Container cover *(Numbers 19:15)* (3)
15 'He… became obedient to death, even death on — — !' *(Philippians 2:8)* (1,5)
19 Refrain *(1 Peter 2:11)* (7)
20 'She began to — his feet with her tears' *(Luke 7:38)* (3)
24 One who worships Brahma, Vishnu or Shiva (5)
25 'Give to everyone who — you' *(Luke 6:30)* (4)
26 'I lift up my eyes to the hills; where does my — come from?' *(Psalm 121:1)* (4)
27 One of those whom the Lord said would be taken from Jerusalem and Judah as judgment on them *(Isaiah 3:2)* (4)

No 55

Across

1 Evil *(Genesis 6:5)* (10)

7 Musician called for by Elisha when he met the kings of Israel, Judah and Edom *(2 Kings 3:15)* (7)

8 The request that led to the institution of the Lord's Prayer: 'Lord, — us to pray' *(Luke 11:1)* (5)

10 'We are hard pressed on every — ' *(2 Corinthians 4:8)* (4)

11 Fraud *(2 Corinthians 6:8)* (8)

13 'His troops advance in force; they build a siege ramp against me and — around my tent' *(Job 19:12)* (6)

15 Where Rachel hid Laban's household gods when he searched his daughter's tent *(Genesis 31:34)* (6)

17 'Now about spiritual gifts, brothers, I do not want you to be — ' *(1 Corinthians 12:1)* (8)

18 Nomadic dwelling *(Genesis 26:25)* (4)

21 'As for man, his days are like — , he flourishes like a flower of the field' *(Psalm 103:15)* (5)

22 Or I live (anag.) (7)

23 Those guilty of 1 Across *(Romans 13:4)* (10)

Down

1 'God so loved the — that he gave his one and only Son' *(John 3:16)* (5)

2 'Away in a manger, no — for a bed' (4)

3 Mob ten (anag.) (6)

4 'Each — group made its own gods in several towns where they settled' *(2 Kings 17:29)* (8)

5 Began *(Luke 9:46)* (7)

6 Speaking very softly *(John 7:32)* (10)

9 Workers Ruth joined when she arrived in Bethlehem with her mother-in-law Naomi *(Ruth 2:3)* (10)

12 Put in jail *(Acts 22:19)* (8)

14 Ace turn (anag.) (7)

16 Discharge *(Acts 21:3)* (6)

19 'All these — come from inside and make a man "unclean"' *(Mark 7:23)* (5)

20 'Let us rejoice and be glad and — him glory!' *(Revelation 19:7)* (4)

No 56

Across

1 Proverbs describes her as being 'of noble character' *(Proverbs 31:10)* (4)

3 'Shall we go up again — — against the Benjamites, our brothers?' *(Judges 20:23)* (2,6)

8 A descendant of Shem *(Genesis 10:28)* (4)

9 'Anyone who does not carry his cross and follow me cannot be my — ' *(Luke 14:27)* (8)

11 Resentment *(Ephesians 4:31)* (10)

14 In Cain (anag.) (6)

15 'Such knowledge is too wonderful for me, too lofty for me to — ' *(Psalm 139:6)* (6)

17 Intense *(1 Thessalonians 4:5)* (10)

20 Third Order of the Roman Catholic Church (8)
21 'At midnight the cry rang out, "Here's the bridegroom! Come out to — him"' *(Matthew 25:6)* (4)
22 'My grace is sufficient for you, for my power is made perfect in — ' *(2 Corinthians 12:9)* (8)
23 'As the — pants for streams of water, so my soul pants for you, O God' *(Psalm 42:1)* (4)

Down

1 Nickname of popular First World War chaplain, the Revd G.A. Studdert Kennedy, — Willie (8)
2 Occasion of religious joy *(Lamentations 2:22)* (5,3)
4 'We three kings of — are' (6)
5 Allegation or charge *(Jude 9)* (10)
6 Kind *(1 Chronicles 12:33)* (4)
7 'Open your — and look at the fields!' *(John 4:35)* (4)
10 Also known as the Feast of Lights *(John 10:22)* (10)
12 Area that saw the healing of two demon-possessed men and a herd of pigs stampeding to their deaths *(Matthew 8:28)* (8)
13 Forebear *(James 2:21)* (8)
16 Name given to the first two books of the Apocrypha (6)
18 Esau sold his birthright for this *(Genesis 25:34)* (4)
19 Rear (anag.) (4)

No 57

Across

8 One of the titles given to the Messiah in Isaiah's prediction *(Isaiah 9:6)* (6,2,5)

9 International Nepal Fellowship (1,1,1)

10 Single *(1 Corinthians 7:27)* (9)

11 Aleksandr Solzhenitsyn's seminal book about Soviet prison camps, *The — Archipelago* (5)

13 Treachery *(2 Kings 11:14)* (7)

16 Of India (anag.) (2,3,2)

19 'God has put us apostles on display at the end of the procession, like men condemned to die in the — ' *(1 Corinthians 4:9)* (5)

22 Follower of a theological system characterized by a strong belief in predestination (9)

24 ‘Put these old rags and worn-out clothes under your arms to — the ropes’ *(Jeremiah 38:12)* (3)

25 They brought together all the elders of the Israelites in Egypt *(Exodus 4:29)* (5,3,5)

Down

1 The season when kings ‘go off to war’ *(2 Samuel 11:1)* (6)

2 Simon Peter’s response to Jesus by the Sea of Galilee: ‘Go away from me, Lord; I am a — man’ *(Luke 5:8)* (6)

3 Beaten with whips *(1 Kings12:11)* (8)

4 ‘You shall not — adultery’ *(Exodus 20:14)* (6)

5 Encourage *(Hebrews 10:24)* (4)

6 Service of morning prayer in the Church of England (6)

7 ‘Take and eat this in remembrance that Christ died for you, and — — him in your heart by faith with thanksgiving’ (4,2)

12 Run (anag.) (3)

14 Member of 17th-century party that denied the right of autonomy to the Church (8)

15 ‘We will triumph with our tongues; we — our lips’ *(Psalm 12:4)* (3)

16 Earnings *(1 Corinthians 16:2)* (6)

17 ‘I rejoice greatly in the Lord that — — you have renewed your concern for me’ *(Philippians 4:10)* (2,4)

18 How Paul described Philemon *(Philemon 1)* (6)

20 Multiple territories under the rule of a single state *(Daniel 11:4)* (6)

21 ‘You have been unfaithful; you have married foreign women, — to Israel’s guilt’ *(Ezra 10:10)* (6)

23 This month (abbrev.) (4)

No 58

Across

1 'Unless the Lord builds the house, its builders — in vain' *(Psalm 127:1)* (6)

4 Season of the year *(Psalm 84:6)* (6)

7 'My soul is overwhelmed with sorrow to the point of death. — here and keep watch with me' *(Matthew 26:38)* (4)

8 It came over the whole land from the sixth to the ninth hour on the first Good Friday *(Luke 23:44)* (8)

9 Paul invariably did this in the synagogues he visited on his missionary journeys *(Acts 17:2)* (8)

13 'It is God who works in you to will and to — according to his good purpose' *(Philippians 2:13)* (3)

16 Members of the Church of Scotland (13)

17 'Now when he saw the crowds, he went up on a mountainside and — down' *(Matthew 5:1)* (3)

19 Mock *(Luke 14:29)* (8)

24 Disgrace *(Psalm 44:13)* (8)

25 First month of the Hebrew calendar *(Exodus 13:4)* (4)

26 Christianity of the Britons before Augustine arrived from Rome (6)

27 Mean *(Numbers 35:23)* (6)

Down

1 'Whoever finds his life will — it' *(Matthew 10:39)* (4)

2 'My lord the king, let the — — on me and on my father's family, and let the king and his throne be without guilt' *(2 Samuel 14:9)* (5,4)

3 O raid (anag.) (5)

4 'If two of you on earth — about anything you ask for, it will be done for you by my Father in heaven' *(Matthew 18:19)* (5)

5 Take care of *(1 Samuel 17:15)* (4)

6 What the older son heard as he came near the house the day his prodigal brother came home *(Luke 15:25)* (5)

10 'Do not think of yourself more highly than you ought, but rather think of yourself with — judgment' *(Romans 12:3)* (5)

11 Do ten (anag.) (5)

12 Architectural style first used in Greek temples in the sixth century BC (5)

13 Capable of being used *(1 Kings 7:36)* (9)

14 'Each one should — his own actions' *(Galatians 6:4)* (4)

15 Among the items imported by Solomon's fleet of trading ships *(1 Kings 10:22)* (4)

18 'But I am afraid that just — — was deceived by the serpent's cunning, your minds may somehow be led astray' *(2 Corinthians 11:3)* (2,3)

20 Outstanding 18th-century hymn writer, — Watts (5)

21 One of the four sons of Asher *(Genesis 46:17)* (5)

22 Be distressed *(Proverbs 24:19)* (4)

23 He was the father of Gaal, who threatened rebellion against Abimelech *(Judges 9:28)* (4)

No 59

Across

1 Tertullus, who presented the high priest's case against Paul in his trial before Felix, was one *(Acts 24:1)* (6)

4 As balm (anag.) (6)

8 Having explored Canaan, he and Joshua urged the Israelites to take possession of it *(Numbers 13:30)* (5)

9 On becoming king of Judah, he had all six of his brothers killed *(2 Chronicles 21:4)* (7)

10 'Even the — has found a home, and the swallow a nest for herself' *(Psalm 84:3)* (7)

11 Banishment *(Jeremiah 29:1)* (5)

12 'And now I will show you the most — way' *(1 Corinthians 12:31)* (9)

17 'Titus did not exploit you, did he? Did we not — — the same spirit and follow the same course?' *(2 Corinthians 12:18)* (3,2)

19 Mice den (anag.) (7)

21 How Egypt is often described in the Old Testament: 'the land of — ' *(Exodus 13:3)* (7)

22 One of the first Levites to resettle in Jerusalem after the exile in Babylon *(1 Chronicles 9:15)* (5)

23 'As a sheep before her shearers is — , so he did not open his mouth' *(Isaiah 53:7)* (6)

24 Paul's birthplace *(Acts 22:3)* (6)

Down

1 Ravenous insect inflicted on Egypt in vast numbers as the eighth plague *(Exodus 10:14)* (6)

2 Well-being *(Philippians 2:20)* (7)

3 Small piece of live coal or wood in a dying fire *(Psalm 102:3)* (5)

5 Sportsman or woman *(2 Timothy 2:5)* (7)

6 The original name of Abraham's wife *(Genesis 17:15)* (5)

7 'So in Christ we who are many form one body, and each — belongs to all the others' *(Romans 12:5)* (6)

9 According to Peter, a wife's beauty should not come from wearing this *(1 Peter 3:3)* (9)

13 'For God did not send his Son into the world to — the world' *(John 3:17)* (7)

14 'The Lord of heaven and earth… does not live in — built by hands' *(Acts 17:24)* (7)

15 'If your hand — you to sin, cut it off' *(Mark 9:43)* (6)

16 Something like these fell from Saul's eyes as soon as Ananias placed his hands on him *(Acts 9:18)* (6)

18 Track *(Job 41:30)* (5)

20 Religious doctrine (5)

No 60

Across

1 'How dare you turn my Father's house — a market!' *(John 2:16)* (4)

3 To administer to babies the Anglican rite signifying their incorporation into the Church (8)

9 'When Joram — — he asked, "Have you come in peace?"' *(2 Kings 9:22)* (3,4)

10 'Do not rejoice that the spirits submit to you, but rejoice that your — are written in heaven' *(Luke 10:20)* (5)

11 Wash *(Leviticus 15:11)* (5)

12 In late (anag.) (6)

14 'Men ate the — — —; he sent them all the food they could eat' *(Psalm 78:25)* (5,2,6)

17 and **15 Down** Your statutes stand firm; holiness — your house for — days, O Lord' *(Psalm 93:5)* (6,7)

19 '"Yes, Lord," she replied, "but even the dogs under the — eat the children's crumbs"' *(Mark 7:28)* (5)

22 Blood-sucking worm *(Proverbs 30:15)* (5)

23 'It seemed good also to me to write an orderly — for you, most excellent Theophilus' *(Luke 1:3)* (7)

24 Gather together *(Numbers 10:3)* (8)

25 'He was a prophet, powerful in word and — before God and all the people' *(Luke 24:19)* (4)

Down

1 Write *(Isaiah 30:8)* (8)

2 'I press on towards the goal — — the prize for which God has called me heavenwards in Christ Jesus' *(Philippians 3:14)* (2,3)

4 'This is the covenant I will make with the — — — after that time, declares the Lord' *(Hebrews 8:10)* (5,2,6)

5 'In my Father's house are many rooms; — it were — so, I would have told you' *(John 14:2)* (2,3)

6 Samson's father-in-law was one *(Judges 15:6)* (7)

7 Noted architect of All Souls, Langham Place, John — (4)

8 Protect *(Zechariah 9:8)* (6)

13 Insisted *(Luke 22:59)* (8)

15 See 17 Across

16 Pilate had one prepared and fastened to Jesus' cross *(John 19:19)* (6)

18 Caleb's great-great-grandson *(1 Chronicles 2:44)* (5)

20 Tuber (anag.) (5)

21 'Just as I am, without one — ' (4)

No 61

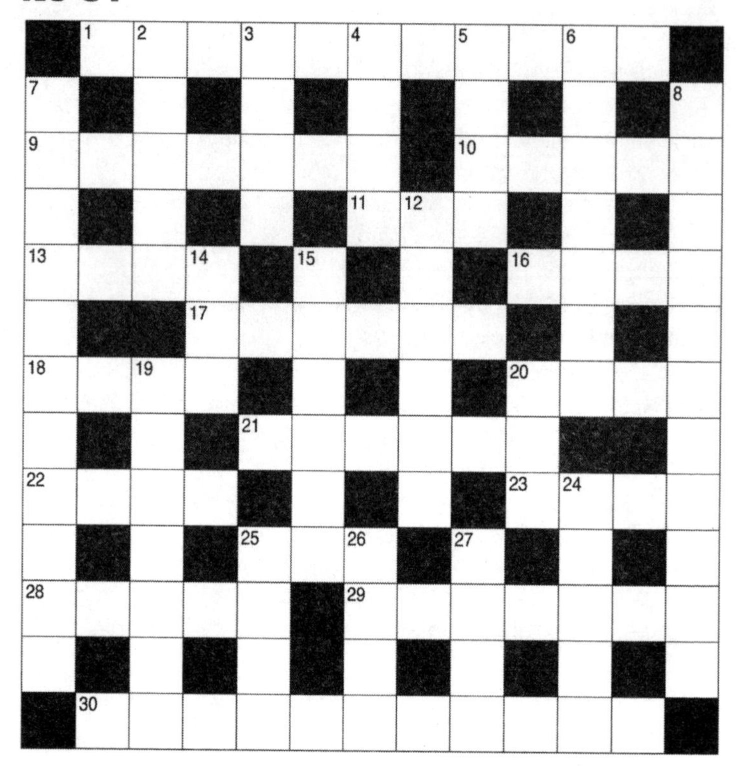

Across

1 Tuition *(2 Timothy 4:2)* (11)

9 'Even the doe in the field deserts her — fawn because there is no grass' *(Jeremiah 14:5)* (7)

10 On Paul's voyage to Rome it lasted 14 days and caused the boat to be shipwrecked *(Acts 27:20)* (5)

11 Writing fluid *(Jeremiah 36:18)* (3)

13 Where the Mount of Olives was in relation to Jerusalem *(Zechariah 14:4)* (4)

16 Oils (anag.) (4)

17 'And God is able to make all grace — to you' *(2 Corinthians 9:8)* (6)

18 Wild goat with backward-curving horns *(Deuteronomy 14:5)* (4)

20 This is what the Lord said he would place 'in the jaws of the peoples' to lead them astray *(Isaiah 30:28)* (1,3)
21 Unjust *(Matthew 20:13)* (6)
22 The intimate name that Jesus used for God *(Mark 14:36)* (4)
23 Mountain on which Joshua built an altar to mark the renewal of God's covenant with Israel *(Joshua 8:30)* (4)
25 'For as in the day of Midian's defeat, you have shattered… the — across their shoulders' *(Isaiah 9:4)* (3)
28 The advice given Job by his wife: 'Are you still holding on to your integrity? — God and die!' *(Job 2:9)* (5)
29 How the Lord described Job's character *(Job 1:8)* (7)
30 The question a Pharisee put to Jesus: 'Teacher, which is the greatest — in the Law?' *(Matthew 22:36)* (11)

Down

2 ' — — the day of salvation' *(2 Corinthians 6:2)* (3,2)
3 For example, hammer *(Isaiah 44:12)* (4)
4 He was one of the lyre players when the ark of God was brought to Jerusalem *(1 Chronicles 15:20)* (4)
5 What Paul wanted to complete before going to Spain *(Romans 15:28)* (4)
6 He assisted Bezalel in the construction of the tabernacle *(Exodus 38:23)* (7)
7 That which is due to an heir *(Ephesians 1:18)* (11)
8 Perpetual existence *(1 Corinthians 15:53)* (11)
12 Fifth-century saint who evangelized the Picts of southern Scotland (6)
14 This was collected by, among others, Matthew *(Matthew 10:3)* (3)
15 One of the women who went to the tomb of Jesus early on Easter morning *(Luke 24:10)* (6)
19 Mob rage (anag.) (7)
20 'Then Nathan said to David, "You — the man!"' *(2 Samuel 12:7)* (3)
24 Started *(Luke 4:31)* (5)
25 Piece of wood used for horizontal support *(Ezra 6:11)* (4)
26 'The wealth of the rich is their fortified city, but poverty is the — of the poor' *(Proverbs 10:15)* (4)
27 A grandson of Noah *(Genesis 10:22)* (4)

No 62

Across

1 September 29: feast day of an angelic saint and occasion of many Anglican ordinations (10)

7 'If the — does not sound a clear call, who will get ready for battle?' *(1 Corinthians 14:8)* (7)

8 Priest in King David's court who had charge of the ark of the covenant *(2 Samuel 15:25)* (5)

10 Status *(1 Chronicles 15:18)* (4)

11 Where Aaron died *(Numbers 33:38)* (5,3)

13 Wood used extensively in the building of the tabernacle *(Exodus 26:15)* (6)

15 '— — for whom the bell tolls; it tolls for thee' (John Donne) (3,3)

17 Where Israel suffered two major defeats at the hands of the Philistines *(1 Samuel 4:1)* (8)

18 A hit (anag.) (4)

21 Eighteenth letter in the Greek alphabet (5)

22 'Hope deferred makes the heart sick, but a longing fulfilled — — — of life' *(Proverbs 13:12)* (2,1,4)

23 'At midnight the cry rang out: "Here's the — ! Come out to meet him!"' *(Matthew 25:6)* (10)

Down

1 'Blessed are those who — , for they will be comforted' *(Matthew 5:4)* (5)

2 Part of the lampstand in the tabernacle, they are described as 'flowerlike' *(Exodus 25:31)* (4)

3 'Let us fix our eyes on Jesus, the — and perfecter of our faith' *(Hebrews 12:2)* (6)

4 Sloth *(Proverbs 12:24)* (8)

5 'Two blind men were sitting by the roadside, — — they heard that Jesus was going by, they shouted' *(Matthew 20:30)* (3,4)

6 Astrologers *(Isaiah 47:13)* (10)

9 They lived by the sea *(Zephaniah 2:6)* (10)

12 Where grapes are grown *(1 Corinthians 9:7)* (8)

14 Green AV (anag.) (7)

16 Observing *(Acts 2:31)* (6)

19 Where Esther was living when she caught the eye of King Xerxes *(Esther 2:8)* (5)

20 A nephew of Abraham *(Genesis 22:22)* (4)

No 63

Across

1 Rahab hid the two Israelite spies under these stalks on the roof of her house in Jericho *(Joshua 2:6)* (4)

3 'Let us then — the throne of grace with confidence' *(Hebrews 4:16)* (8)

8 Attack *(2 Samuel 3:22)* (4)

9 'They devoted themselves to the apostles' — and to the fellowship' *(Acts 2:42)* (8)

11 These occupied the Israelites for 40 years (10)

14 Rented *(Song of Songs 8:11)* (3,3)

15 Rimmed (anag.) (6)

17 Complimentary *(Psalm 12:2)* (10)

20 One who pleads another's cause *(Job 16:19)* (8)

21 Where Martin Luther refused to recant his supposedly heretical teachings in 1521, the — of Worms (4)
22 'Honest scales and — are from the Lord; all the weights in the bag are of his making' *(Proverbs 16:11)* (8)
23 One of Abram's allies in his campaign to rescue Lot, taken in battle *(Genesis 14:13)* (4)

Down

1 Goodbye *(Acts 15:29)* (8)
2 Estrange *(Galatians 4:17)* (8)
4 Job, Psalms, Proverbs, Ecclesiastes, Song of Songs, so-called — books of the Bible (6)
5 Identified *(Acts 12:14)* (10)
6 'See — the winter snow, born for us on earth below' (4)
7 'Therefore, since we have a great — priest who has gone through the heavens, Jesus the Son of God' *(Hebrews 4:14)* (4)
10 Ban lip cure (anag.) (10)
12 Paul condemned this aspiration when it was selfish *(Galatians 5:20)* (8)
13 How Paul described the light he saw on the road to Damascus, in relation to the sun *(Acts 26:13)* (8)
16 The one in Nebuchadnezzar's dream was described as 'awesome in appearance' *(Daniel 2:31)* (6)
18 Vocal parts in a choir (initials) (1,1,1,1)
19 'And lead us not into temptation, but deliver us from the — one' *(Matthew 6:13)* (4)

No 64

Across

8 Jesus was criticized for eating with these people *(Matthew 9:11)* (3,10)

9 'And surely I am with you always, to the very — of the age' *(Matthew 28:20)* (3)

10 Extreme *(Psalm 142:6)* (9)

11 Among other things, the sound of the horn, flute, zither, lyre, pipes and harp *(Daniel 3:5)* (5)

13 Charged *(Mark 15:3)* (7)

16 'The spirit is — , but the body is weak' *(Matthew 26:41)* (7)

19 'On the eighth day, when it was time to circumcise him, he was — Jesus' *(Luke 2:21)* (5)

22 Bid is evil (anag.) (9)

24 Appropriate *(Proverbs 15:23)* (3)
25 Role assigned to the Gibeonites as punishment for deceiving the Israelites *(Joshua 9:23)* (5-8)

Down

1 'But let justice roll on like a river, righteousness like a never-failing — ' (Amos 5:24) (6)
2 Comes between Genesis and Leviticus (6)
3 He adopted Esther on the death of her parents *(Esther 2:15)* (8)
4 'The spirit of Elijah is resting on — ' *(2 Kings 2:15)* (6)
5 Measured area of land *(1 Samuel 14:14)* (4)
6 Paul was handed over to them in Jerusalem *(Acts 28:17)* (6)
7 'Who may — the hill of the Lord? Who may stand in his holy place?' *(Psalm 24:3)* (6)
12 Father of Bezalel, chosen by God to head up the building of the tabernacle *(Exodus 31:2)* (3)
14 'How skilled you are at pursuing love! Even the worst of women — — from your ways' *(Jeremiah 2:33)* (3,5)
15 Jesus described it as 'the lamp of your body' *(Luke 11:34)* (3)
16 Looking after these women was what James described as 'pure and faultless religion' *(James 1:27)* (6)
17 A descendant of the third son of Jacob and Leah *(Exodus 2:1)* (6)
18 Where the son of Aaron was buried *(Joshua 24:33)* (6)
20 Lamented *(Isaiah 38:14)* (6)
21 Tested (anag.) (6)
23 'Now faith is being — of what we hope for' *(Hebrews 11:1)* (4)

No 65

Across

1 'He measured its wall and it was 144 — thick' *(Revelation 21:17)* (6)

4 'As long as the earth endures… cold and heat, — and winter, day and night will never cease' *(Genesis 8:22)* (6)

7 Before God's pronouncement in 2 Across, this fell on the earth for 40 days and nights *(Genesis 7:12)* (4)

8 Unnecessary *(1 Samuel 25:31)* (8)

9 He was in charge of the forced labour used to build the temple in Jerusalem *(1 Kings 5:14)* (8)

13 Church's Ministry among the Jews (1,1,1)

16 'He makes me lie down in — — , he leads me beside quiet waters' *(Psalm 23:2)* (5,8)

17 Affirmative (2 *Corinthians 1:20)* (3)

19 Short sermons (8)
24 Or the hit (anag.) (8)
25 Pierce *(Zechariah 13:3)* (4)
26 'You — out a gnat but swallow a camel' *(Matthew 23:24)* (6)
27 'To this end I labour, struggling with all his — , which so powerfully works in me' *(Colossians 1:29)* (6)

Down

1 'O Lord, what is man that you — for him, the son of man that you think of him?' *(Psalm 144:3)* (4)
2 Condition that afflicted Bartimaeus *(Mark 10:46)* (9)
3 and **22** The two basic groups of Islam (5,4)
4 This queen visited Solomon and lavished gifts on him *(1 Kings 10:10)* (5)
5 'If someone forces you to go one — , go with him two' *(Matthew 5:41)* (4)
6 Mopes (anag.) (5)
10 At this hour, Jesus cried from the cross, 'Eloi, Eloi, lama sabachthani?' *(Mark 15:34)* (5)
11 Kingdom *(Joshua 13:21)* (5)
12 The Sea in the temple (a great basin) was made of this *(1 Kings 7:23)* (5)
13 Jesus followed his father into this trade *(Mark 6:3)* (9)
14 'Great and marvellous are your deeds, Lord God Almighty. — and true are your ways' *(Revelation 15:3)* (4)
15 These cows ate up the seven fat cows in Pharaoh's dream *(Genesis 41:20)* (4)
18 Decree *(Daniel 6:7)* (5)
20 His son Pagiel assisted Moses and Aaron in taking a census of the Israelites *(Numbers 1:13)* (5)
21 'Prepare a guest room for me, because — — to be restored to you in answer to your prayers' *(Philemon 22)* (1,4)
22 See 3 Down
23 'What kind of man is this? Even the winds and the waves — him' *(Matthew 8:27)* (4)

No 66

Across

1 'Therefore, I urge you, brothers, in view of God's mercy, to offer your — as living sacrifices' *(Romans 12:1)* (6)

4 Uttered *(Psalm 60:6)* (6)

8 Representative *(Nehemiah 11:24)* (5)

9 Ardent *(Proverbs 26:23)* (7)

10 My paint (anag.) (7)

11 Animals often used as burnt offerings *(Numbers 29:13)* (5)

12 'Jesus turned and said to them, " — of Jerusalem, do not weep for me"' *(Luke 23:28)* (9)

17 See 23 Across

19 Samuel's father *(1 Samuel 1:19)* (7)

21 'The angel of the Lord — around those who fear him' *(Psalm 34:7)* (7)

22 'I am the Alpha and the — ' *(Revelation 1:8)* (5)

23 and **17** 'If someone strikes you on one cheek, — — him the other also. If someone takes your — , do not stop him from taking your tunic' *(Luke 6:28)* (4,2,5)

24 Upward slope *(Nehemiah 12:37)* (6)

Down

1 Queen Vashti was noted for this quality *(Esther 1:11)* (6)

2 'The king summoned the magicians, enchanters, sorcerers and astrologers to tell him what he had — ' *(Daniel 2:2)* (7)

3 Additional *(Mark 6:9)* (5)

5 For example, the Lost Sheep *(Luke 15:3)* (7)

6 'Come, let us bow down in worship, let us — before the Lord our Maker' *(Psalm 95:6)* (5)

7 'But Ahaz said, "I will — —; I will not put the Lord to the test"' *(Isaiah 7:12)* (3,3)

9 Lacking trust (2 *Timothy 2:13)* (9)

13 Dishevelled *(Leviticus 10:6)* (7)

14 'Love must be — . Hate what is evil; cling to what is good' *(Romans 12:9)* (7)

15 It gave away Peter's identity in the high priest's courtyard at the trial of Jesus *(Matthew 26:73)* (6)

16 Frustrate *(Isaiah 14:27)* (6)

18 Happen *(1 Corinthians 5:1)* (5)

20 'And he who searches our hearts — the mind of the Spirit' *(Romans 8:27)* (5)

No 67

Across

1 It was during this that Jesus washed his disciples' feet *(John 13:4)* (4)

3 'It will produce branches and bear fruit and become a — cedar' *(Ezekiel 17:23)* (8)

9 Normal, customary or usual *(Job 1:5)* (7)

10 'He has granted — — life to rebuild the house of our God' *(Ezra 9:9)* (2,3)

11 Excessive desire condemned by Christ *(Luke 11:39)* (5)

12 Nothing of this nature will ever enter the new Jerusalem *(Revelation 21:27)* (6)

14 'May the words of my mouth and — — of my heart be pleasing in your sight' *(Psalm 19:14)* (3,10)

17 Founder of the Missionaries of Charity, Mother — (6)

19 'Create in me a pure heart, O God, and — a steadfast spirit within me' *(Psalm 51:10)* (5)

22 Dot it (anag.) (5)

23 One who enters a country by force *(Daniel 11:16)* (7)

24 He sold everything he had in order to buy a pearl of great value *(Matthew 13:45–46)* (8)

25 'Let's make a small room on the roof and put in it — — and a table' *(2 Kings 4:10)* (1,3)

Down

1 'In preaching the gospel I may offer it free of charge, and so not make use of — — in preaching it' *(1 Corinthians 9:18)* (2,6)

2 Debate, contend *(Acts 6:9)* (5)

4 'Is not the bread that we break a — in the body of Christ?' *(1 Corinthians 10:16)* (13)

5 'May the God of peace… that great Shepherd of the sheep, — you with everything good for doing his will' *(Hebrews 13:20–21)* (5)

6 Roman coins *(Luke 7:41)* (7)

7 Daybreak *(John 8:2)* (4)

8 Formal promise *(Numbers 30:2)* (6)

13 Replied *(Matthew 4:4)* (8)

15 Let core (anag.) (7)

16 'Then, when I — , I will give letters of introduction to the men you approve and send them with your gift to Jerusalem' *(1 Corinthians 16:3)* (6)

18 He was taken up bodily to heaven *(Genesis 5:24)* (5)

20 Aaron's son *(Exodus 6:23)* (5)

21 The first man *(Genesis 2:20)* (4)

No 68

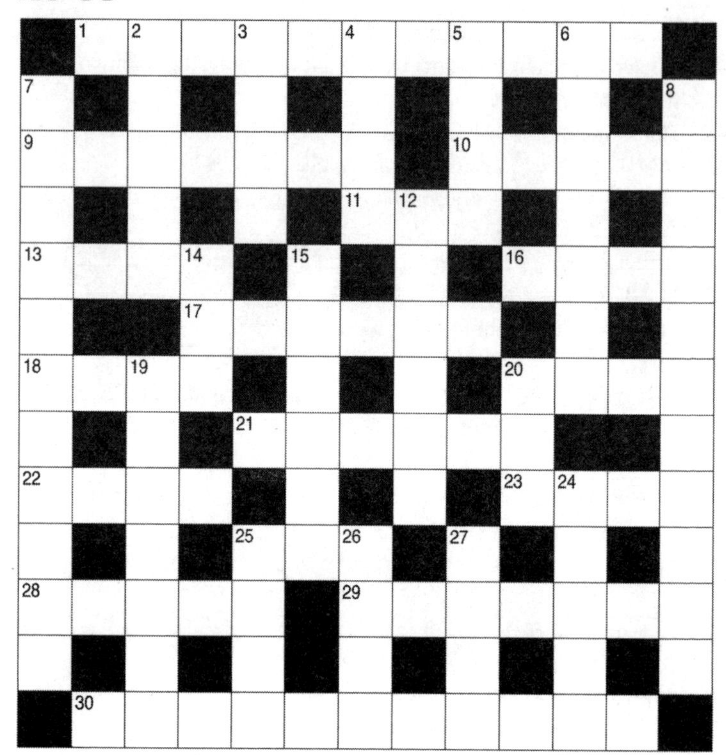

Across

1 'Christ crucified: a stumbling-block to Jews and — to Gentiles' *(1 Corinthians 1:23)* (11)

9 Set turn (anag.) (6)

10 Associated with the neighbourhood *(Matthew 10:17)* (5)

11 She was 'deceived by the serpent's cunning' *(2 Corinthians 11:3)* (3)

13 'If a man shuts his — to the cry of the poor, he too will cry out and not be answered' *(Proverbs 21:13)* (4)

16 Persuade gently *(Judges 14:15)* (4)

17 'Don't be —; you are worth more than many sparrows' *(Luke 12:7)* (6)

18 'Every precious stone adorned you: — , topaz and emerald' *(Ezekiel 28:13)* (4)

20 Deliberately avoid *(Job 28:28)* (4)

21 'When he — — his senses, he said, "How many of my father's hired men have food to spare…"' *(Luke 15:17)* (4,2)

22 Stop (anag.) (4)

23 Close to *(Numbers 17:13)* (4)

25 'Woe to the women who — magic charms on all their wrists' *(Ezekiel 13:18)* (3)

28 'I am like an — tree flourishing in the house of God' *(Psalm 52:8)* (5)

29 One of the seven eunuchs who served King Xerxes *(Esther 1:10)* (7)

30 'We are therefore Christ's — ' *(2 Corinthians 5:20)* (11)

Down

2 The garment that Peter wrapped around him when he left his fishing boat to greet Jesus *(John 21:7)* (5)

3 'When Jesus had cried out again in a — voice, he gave up his spirit' *(Matthew 27:50)* (4)

4 Location or place *(Genesis 12:6)* (4)

5 The water of this river changed to blood when Moses struck it with his staff *(Exodus 7:20)* (4)

6 City in the Jordan Valley whose elders were punished by Gideon for refusing to feed his troops *(Judges 8:16)* (7)

7 'Saul and all the Israelites held a great — ' *(1 Samuel 11:15)* (11)

8 'The centurion found an — ship sailing for Italy' *(Acts 27:6)* (11)

12 Concealed *(2 Corinthians 4:3)* (6)

14 Speak *(Numbers 22:38)* (3)

15 ' — in me a pure heart, O God' *(Psalm 51:10)* (6)

19 'There is one body and one Spirit, one Lord, one faith, one — ' *(Ephesians 4:4–5)* (7)

20 'Surely this man was the — of God' *(Mark 15:39)* (3)

24 Come or go into *(Psalm 100:4)* (5)

25 'Let us — — king over us like all the nations around us' *(Deuteronomy 17:14)* (3,1)

26 'The crooked roads shall become straight, the rough — smooth' *(Luke 3:5)* (4)

27 Disaster struck the man who built his house on this *(Matthew 7:26)* (4)

No 69

Across

1 Instructions *(1 Corinthians 11:34)* (10)

7 Mistaken *(Mark 12:24)* (2,5)

8 Due to (anag.) (5)

10 Where in his garment a person might carry consecrated meat *(Haggai 2:12)* (4)

11 A day's pay in the vineyard *(Matthew 20:2)* (8)

13 'She wrapped him in — and placed him in a manger' *(Luke 2:7)* (6)

15 Indian state where Baptist pioneer missionary William Carey first landed in 1793 (6)

17 What the large crowd did when Jesus taught in the temple courts *(Mark 12:37)* (8)

18 Pots (anag.) (4)

21 'Your sons and daughters will prophesy, your — men will see visions' *(Acts 2:17)* (5)

22 'I cry aloud to the Lord; I lift up my — — the Lord for mercy' *(Psalm 142:1)* (5,2)

23 Observed (for example, the Passover) *(Joshua 5:10)* (10)

Down

1 'I will — in the house of the Lord for ever' *(Psalm 23:6)* (5)

2 How the word of the Lord was described at the time the young Samuel ministered in the temple *(1 Samuel 3:1)* (4)

3 'The fig-tree you — has withered!' *(Mark 11:21)* (6)

4 According to Paul, such a person has no 'inheritance in the kingdom of Christ and of God' *(Ephesians 5:5)* (8)

5 'Great peace have they who love your law, and — can make them stumble' *(Psalm 119:165)* (7)

6 Paul and Barnabas experienced this in trying to keep the crowd from sacrificing to them *(Acts 14:18)* (10)

9 A familiar refrain from Daniel quoted by Jesus: 'the abomination that causes — ' *(Matthew 24:15)* (10)

12 'Does — — soar at your command and build his nest on high?' *(Job 39:27)* (3,5)

14 Unclear *(Ezekiel 3:5)* (7)

16 'Like a — I have rolled up my life, and he has cut me off from the loom' *(Isaiah 38:12)* (6)

19 Appeal earnestly *(Daniel 2:18)* (5)

20 Jesus said that this should be offered only after a person has been reconciled with his or her brother *(Matthew 5:24)* (4)

No 70

Across

1 He was commander-in-chief of David's army *(1 Chronicles 11:6)* (4)

3 Famous church in London's Langham Place (3,5)

8 Globe *(Isaiah 22:18)* (4)

9 'For there the Lord bestows his blessing, even life for — ' *(Psalm 133:3)* (8)

11 'You are to abstain from food — to idols' *(Acts 15:29)* (10)

14 'You are worthy — — the scroll and to open its seals' *(Revelation 5:9)* (2,4)

15 'Without faith it is impossible to — God' *(Hebrews 11:6)* (6)

17 In Paul's view the Gentiles had given themselves over to this *(Ephesians 4:19)* (10)

20 'The chief priests and the elders of the people came to the — to put Jesus to death' *(Matthew 27:1)* (8)
21 Goliath was one to the Philistines *(1 Samuel 17:51)* (4)
22 Where God placed a cherubim to guard the way to the tree of life in the garden of Eden *(Genesis 3:24)* (4,4)
23 Dues (anag.) (4)

Down

1 Araunah, on whose threshing floor David built an altar to the Lord, was one *(2 Samuel 24:18)* (8)
2 Assign *(Joshua 13:6)* (8)
4 'If we love one another, God lives in us and his — — made complete in us' *(1 John 4:12)* (4,2)
5 'Those who — at the — share in what is offered' *(1 Corinthians 9:13)* (5,5)
6 'Cast your bread — the waters, for after many days you will find it again' *(Ecclesiastes 11:1)* (4)
7 What the farmer went out to sow *(Mark 4:3)* (4)
10 Diseases *(Luke 5:15)* (10)
12 Indolence *(Proverbs 19:15)* (8)
13 'God saw all that he had made, and it was — — ' *(Genesis 1:31)* (4,4)
16 'The wicked man flees though no one pursues, but the righteous are — — as a lion' *(Proverbs 28:1)* (2,4)
18 'People begged him to let the sick touch the — of his cloak, and all who touched him were healed' *(Matthew 14:35–36)* (4)
19 Cats (anag.) (4)

No 71

Across

8 Oholibamah was the daughter of Anah and — of Zibeon *(Genesis 36:14)* (13)

9 Possess *(Genesis 30:43)* (3)

10 Official name of the Mormons: The Church of Jesus Christ of — — Saints (6-3)

11 'The Lord has — with me according to my righteousness' *(Psalm 18:20)* (5)

13 Rap soon (anag.) (7)

16 Put off until later *(Isaiah 46:13)* (7)

19 The basket containing the baby Moses was placed among these along the banks of the Nile *(Exodus 2:3)* (5)

22 'Even the — Abraham gave him a tenth of the plunder' *(Hebrews 7:4)* (9)

24 He was David's priest (2 *Samuel 20:25)* (3)

25 He was enthroned as Archbishop of Canterbury in February 2003 (5,8)

Down

1 'The ancient mountains crumbled and the — hills collapsed' *(Habakkuk 3:6)* (3-3)

2 C.S. Lewis' mysterious world beyond the wardrobe (6)

3 Paul urged the Christians of Corinth to flee from this *(1 Corinthians 10:14)* (8)

4 Third and best-known part of the 14th-century Italian classic *The Divine Comedy*, — Inferno (6)

5 He was the father of Shannah, one of David's three mighty men *(2 Samuel 23:11)* (4)

6 Distance of about 202 yards in New Testament times, from which we get our word for arenas *(Revelation 14:20)* (6)

7 'Then Simon answered, " — — the Lord for me"' *(Acts 8:24)* (4,2)

12 'The — cannot say to the hand, "I don't need you!"' *(1 Corinthians 12:21)* (3)

14 Let or hop (anag.) (8)

15 The land where Cain went to live, east of Eden *(Genesis 4:16)* (3)

16 'I desire to — and be with Christ' *(Philippians 1:23)* (6)

17 They left Zoar and settled in the mountains, — and his — daughters *(Genesis 19:30)* (3,3)

18 Author of *The Origin of Species by Means of Natural Selection*, Charles — (6)

20 He successfully confronted 450 prophets of Baal on Mount Carmel *(1 Kings 18:25)* (6)

21 Scanty (6)

23 Scottish island that gives its name to a Christian community (4)

No 72

Across

1 What youths did to Elisha on the road to Bethel *(2 Kings 2:23)* (6)

4 'On this rock I will build my — , and the gates of Hades will not overcome it' *(Matthew 16:18)* (6)

7 Employ *(Matthew 20:1)* (4)

8 Philemon's runaway slave *(Philemon 10)* (8)

9 Jacob deceived his father Isaac into giving him one *(Genesis 27:30)* (8)

13 'Adam named his wife Eve, because — would become the mother of all the living' *(Genesis 3:20)* (3)

16 Nabal was doing this in Carmel when David's men approached him *(1 Samuel 25:7)* (5-8)

17 Set *(Ezekiel 9:2)* (3)

19 Ruling as sovereign *(Matthew 2:22)* (8)

24 Bragging *(James 4:16)* (8)

25 Secure *(Colossians 2:5)* (4)

26 Member of a Jewish cult that flourished at the time of Christ (6)

27 'I would give you spiced wine to drink, the — of my pomegranates' *(Song of Songs 8:2)* (6)

Down

1 He was anointed king of Israel by a prophet in Ramoth Gilead *(2 Kings 9:6)* (4)

2 Registration *(2 Chronicles 17:14)* (9)

3 Scum *(Ezekiel 22:18)* (5)

4 'Lord, if you are willing, you can make me — ' *(Matthew 8:2)* (5)

5 'The body is a — , though it is made up of many parts' *(1 Corinthians 12:12)* (4)

6 'He will — your head, and you will strike his heel' *(Genesis 3:15)* (5)

10 How Paul described his rival apostles in Corinth *(2 Corinthians 11:5)* (5)

11 One of David's thirty chief men *(2 Samuel 23:29)* (5)

12 What the rich fool in Jesus' parable planned to store in his bigger barns *(Luke 12:18)* (5)

13 It is scent (anag.) (9)

14 '[The ostrich] lays her — on the ground and lets them warm in the sand' *(Job 39:14)* (4)

15 What Isaac called the first well dug by his servants in the Valley of Gerar *(Genesis 26:20)* (4)

18 'Dear children, keep yourself from — ' *(1 John 5:21)* (5)

20 Superior class *(Ezekiel 23:7)* (5)

21 'I will summon a sword against — — all my mountains, declares the Sovereign Lord' *(Ezekiel 38:21)* (3,2)

22 Lies (anag.) (4)

23 Unit by which manna was measured *(Exodus 16:32)* (4)

No 73

Across

1 'When we cried out to the Lord, he heard — — and sent an angel and brought us out of Egypt' *(Numbers 20:16)* (3,3)

4 Amazed and horrified *(Isaiah 13:8)* (6)

8 Hand digit *(Leviticus 8:23)* (5)

9 According to the Beloved, this is what the Lover does among the lilies *(Song of Songs 2:16)* (7)

10 'If [your enemy] is thirsty, give him something to drink. — — this, you will heap burning coals on his head' *(Romans 12:20)* (2,5)

11 Tenth *(Leviticus 27:30)* (5)

12 Where some early Christians fled to escape persecution *(Acts 11:19)* (9)

17 A hurry *(Deuteronomy 16:3)* (5)

19 Beseech *(2 Corinthians 5:20)* (7)

21 Alerting *(Acts 20:31)* (7)

22 'So that — I have preached to others, I myself will not be disqualified for the prize' *(1 Corinthians 9:27)* (5)

23 Creative ability *(Acts 17:29)* (6)

24 Twice Gideon used one to test God *(Judges 6:39)* (6)

Down

1 'Make plans by seeking advice; if you wage war, — guidance' *(Proverbs 20:18)* (6)

2 Unproud (anag.) (5,2)

3 How Judas addressed Jesus when he betrayed him in Gethsemane *(Mark 14:45)* (5)

5 Follower of second-century heretical version of Christianity (7)

6 Sates (anag.) (5)

7 'Now that you have — that the Lord is good' *(1 Peter 2:3)* (6)

9 'In the — God created the heavens and the earth' *(Genesis 1:1)* (9)

13 Unlocking *(1 Chronicles 9:27)* (7)

14 Paul said he had been called to be one *(Romans 1:1)* (7)

15 'The devil took him to a very high mountain and — him all the kingdoms of the world' *(Matthew 4:8)* (6)

16 Issued by Caesar Augustus in the year Jesus was born *(Luke 2:1)* (6)

18 In the parable about the rich man and Lazarus, Jesus said the latter was covered with these *(Luke 16:20)* (5)

20 In John's vision, each of the gates of the new Jerusalem was a single one *(Revelation 21:21)* (5)

No 74

Across

1 The son of Jerahmeel and Atarah *(1 Chronicles 2:26)* (4)

3 'For you became sorrowful as God intended and so were not — — any way by us' *(2 Corinthians 7:9)* (6,2)

9 Ruler of the Roman empire *(Acts 25:25)* (7)

10 'They have ears, but cannot hear, — , but they cannot smell' *(Psalm 115:6)* (5)

11 Hold *(Isaiah 2:6)* (5)

12 Absalom's mother *(2 Samuel 3:3)* (6)

14 They went together to ask Pharaoh to let the Israelites leave Egypt *(Exodus 7:10)* (5,3,5)

17 Keeps out of the way of *(Proverbs 16:6)* (6)

19 Border city in the tribal location of Asher *(Joshua 19:27)* (5)

22 'Therefore God exalted him to the highest place and gave him a name that is — every name' *(Philippians 2:9)* (5)

23 The city clerk of Ephesus warned the anti-Paul crowd that they might be charged with this *(Acts 19.40)* (7)

24 'The glorious riches of this mystery, which is — — you, the hope of glory' *(Colossians 1:27)* (6,2)

25 'It is also written: "Do not put the Lord your God to the — "' *(Matthew 4:7)* (4)

Down

1 Conquer *(1 John 2:13)* (8)

2 'I am the — and the Omega' *(Revelation 1:8)* (5)

4 They set out from Haran for the land of Canaan in obedience to God *(Genesis 12:4,5)* (5,3,5)

5 Food provided by God for the Israelites in the wilderness *(Exodus 16:31)* (5)

6 An emotion which, despite enormous difficulties, Paul claimed he did not experience *(2 Corinthians 4:8)* (7)

7 'The infant will play near the hole of the cobra, and the young child put his hand into the viper's — ' *(Isaiah 11:8)* (4)

8 The fruit of the vine *(Job 15:33)* (6)

13 'Throughout the night the cloud brought darkness to the one side — — to the other' *(Exodus 14:20)* (3,5)

15 How the angel described to the shepherds the baby born in Bethlehem *(Luke 2:11)* (7)

16 'We have this hope as an — for the soul' *(Hebrews 6:19)* (6)

18 Aside (anag.) (5)

20 Something the Israelites were told not to accept *(Exodus 23:8)* (5)

21 Missions Advanced Research and Communication (1,1,1,1)

No 75

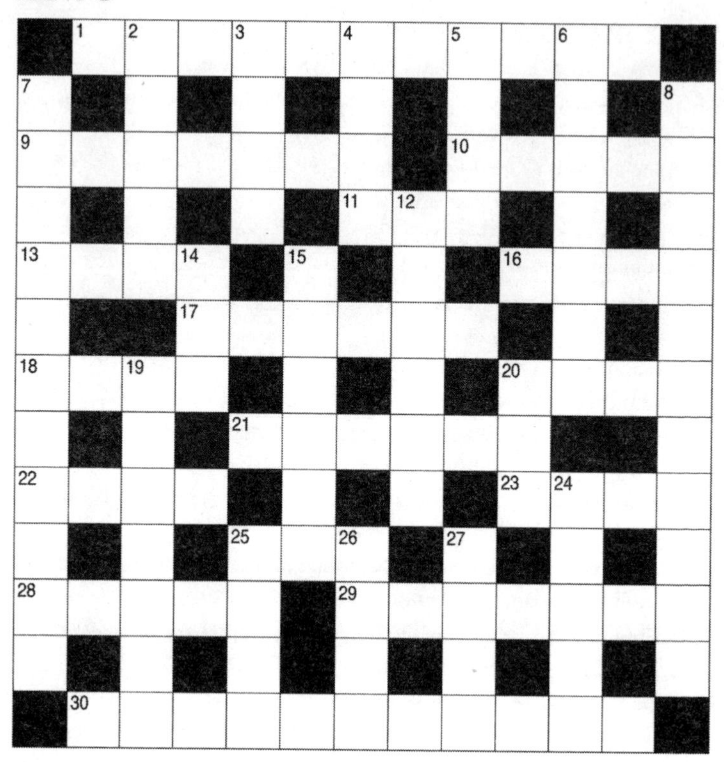

Across

1 Being cleared of blame *(Psalm 17:2)* (11)

9 Hagar put him under a bush to die *(Genesis 21:15)* (7)

10 'Lord, we don't know — you are going' *(John 14:5)* (5)

11 'What is — that you are mindful of him?' *(Psalm 8:4)* (3)

13 One who inherits *(2 Samuel 14:7)* (4)

16 'In my Father's house are many rooms; if — were not — , I would have told you' *(John 14:2)* (2,2)

17 Joins together *(1 Corinthians 6:16)* (6)

18 'I have fought the good fight, I have finished the — , I have kept the faith' *(2 Timothy 4:7)* (4)

20 Laban tricked Jacob into marrying her *(Genesis 29:25)* (4)

21 Relaxed *(Lamentations 1:5)* (2,4)

22 Puss (anag.) (4)

23 See 25 Across

25 and **23 Across** 'Why have you — a — for my life to bring about my death?' *(1 Samuel 28:9)* (3,4)

28 'It is better to take refuge in the Lord than to — in man' *(Psalm 118:8)* (5)

29 The crowd's greeting to Jesus as he rode into Jerusalem on a donkey *(Matthew 21:9)* (7)

30 'Some of the Levites were — , scribes and doorkeepers' *(2 Chronicles 34:13)* (11)

Down

2 Saul's second son *(1 Samuel 14:49)* (5)

3 'A Samaritan woman came to — water' *(John 4:7)* (4)

4 'The storm subsided, and all was — ' *(Luke 8:24)* (4)

5 For example, Nazareth *(Luke 1:26)* (4)

6 'I wept and wept because no one was found who was worthy to — — scroll or look inside' *(Revelation 5:4)* (4,3)

7 Southern Moabite city attacked but not taken by the armies of Israel, Judah and Edom *(2 Kings 3:25)* (3,8)

8 A king of Judah of whom it was said that 'he did what was right in the eyes of the Lord' *(2 Chronicles 20:32)* (11)

12 King to whom the governor of Damascus was responsible at the time of Paul's escape from the city *(2 Corinthians 11:32)* (6)

14 Garden herb *(Luke 11:42)* (3)

15 See 20 Down

19 Take control of *(2 Samuel 12:28)* (7)

20 and **15 Down** 'Jesus said, " — the — children come to me, and do not hinder them"' *(Matthew 19:14)* (3,6)

24 'How blessed you will be, sowing your seed by every stream, and letting your cattle and donkeys — free' *(Isaiah 32:20)* (5)

25 See 26 Down

26 and **25 Down** 'The former preach Christ out of selfish ambition, supposing — they can — up trouble for me while I am in chains' *(Philippians 1:17)* (4,4)

27 Sure (anag.) (4)

No 76

Across

1 Disasters *(1 Samuel 10:19)* (10)

7 Convinced *(Acts 2:36)* (7)

8 What birds do in the branches of a tree *(Matthew 13:32)* (5)

10 Great-great-great-grandfather of Joseph *(Matthew 1:14)* (4)

11 'I will bless her and will surely give you a son by her. I will bless her so that she will — the — of nations' *(Genesis 17:16)* (2,6)

13 Almost *(Acts 21:27)* (6)

15 'Why does this generation ask for a miraculous sign? I tell you the truth, no — will — given to it' *(Mark 8:12)* (4,2)

17 Dusk *(Proverbs 7:9)* (8)

18 Closed *(Genesis 19:6)* (4)

21 Something Paul says a radiant church will not have *(Ephesians 5:27)* (5)
22 And a ram (anag.) (7)
23 God's message through the prophet Amos was that he could not stand these *(Amos 5:21)* (10)

Down

1 Father of the prophet Zephaniah *(Zephaniah 1:1)* (5)
2 Musical instrument *(Psalm 92:3)* (4)
3 Lunatics *(1 Samuel 21:15)* (6)
4 'The plans of the diligent lead — — as surely as haste leads to poverty' *(Proverbs 21:5)* (2,6)
5 'They build — ramps and capture them' *(Habakkuk 1:10)* (7)
6 Original inhabitants of the promised land *(Numbers 21:3)* (10)
9 'I knew that you are a hard man, — where you have not sown' *(Matthew 25:24)* (10)
12 A fleet of trading ships constructed by the kings of Judah and Israel was destroyed because of this *(2 Chronicles 20:37)* (8)
14 They entered the ark two by two *(Genesis 7:8)* (7)
16 Member of the second order of angels *(Ezekiel 10:14)* (6)
19 A shed (anag.) (5)
20 Father of Zaccur, who helped rebuild the walls of Jerusalem *(Nehemiah 3:2)* (4)

No 77

Across

1 One of Lamech's two wives *(Genesis 4:19)* (4)

3 What Paul urged the Christians in Colosse to be in relation to prayer *(Colossians 4:2)* (8)

8 He lives in the Vatican (4)

9 'If anyone does not know how to manage his own family, how can he — — of God's church?' *(1 Timothy 3:5)* (4,4)

11 Inhabitants of the city whose church was condemned for being lukewarm *(Revelation 3:16)* (10)

14 Vigour *(Colossians 1:29)* (6)

15 'Though they plot evil against you and — wicked schemes, they cannot succeed' *(Psalm 21:11)* (6)

17 Paul tells those with this gift to 'govern diligently' *(Romans 12:8)* (10)

20 She prompted her daughter to ask for the head of John the Baptist *(Matthew 14:6)* (8)

21 'After the earthquake came a — ' *(1 Kings 19:12)* (4)

22 Jesus said that this would be an emotion experienced greatly in the run-up to the end of the age *(Matthew 24:21)* (8)

23 'The owl will nest there and lay — , she will hatch them, and care for her young under the shadow of her wings' *(Isaiah 34:15)* (4)

Down

1 Shocked and horrified *(Daniel 8:27)* (8)

2 Commends *(Romans 14:22)* (8)

4 Astonished *(Acts 2:12)* (6)

5 'He who has — hands and a pure — , who does not lift up his soul to an idol or swear by what is false' *(Psalm 24:4)* (5,5)

6 Defect *(Deuteronomy 17:1)* (4)

7 How the devil is described: 'father of — ' *(John 8:44)* (4)

10 Tertullus described Paul to Felix as 'a — of the Nazarene sect' *(Acts 24:5)* (10)

12 'He saw the Spirit of God descending like a dove and — upon him' *(Matthew 3:16)* (8)

13 Vulnerable *(Matthew 9:36)* (8)

16 Ladies (anag.) (6)

18 'Through [Christ] to reconcile to himself all things... by making peace through his blood, — on the cross' *(Colossians 1:20)* (4)

19 'He threw his — around him' *(Luke 15:20)* (4)

No 78

Across

1 Exhilarated *(1 Samuel 11:9)* (6)

4 This filled Saul's heart when he saw the Philistine army at Shunem *(1 Samuel 28:5)* (6)

7 Jesus emitted this when he healed the deaf and mute man *(Mark 7:34)* (4)

8 Aramaic name for the Stone Pavement where Pilate pronounced judgment on Jesus *(John 19:13)* (8)

9 '[Jeremiah] — all these words to me, and I wrote them in ink on the scroll' *(Jeremiah 36:18)* (8)

13 World Evangelical Fellowship (1,1,1)

16 'When the — — saw what had happened, they were greatly distressed and went and told their master' *(Matthew 18:31)* (5,8)

17 Jacob's seventh-born son, the first by Leah's maidservant Zilpah *(Genesis 30:10–11)* (3)

19 For example, springbok, gazelle *(Deuteronomy 14:5)* (8)

24 The psalmist recalls the occasion when swarms of flies did this to the Egyptians *(Psalm 78:45)* (8)

25 Cure *(Luke 10:9)* (4)

26 Stink *(Isaiah 34:3)* (6)

27 'The blind receive sight, the lame walk... the deaf hear, the dead are — ' *(Luke 7:22)* (6)

Down

1 'You have plenty of good things laid up for many years. Take life — ; eat, drink and be merry' *(Luke 12:19)* (4)

2 Agonized *(Daniel 6:20)* (9)

3 Go mad (anag.) (5)

4 'You prepare a — before me in the presence of my enemies' *(Psalm 23:5)* (5)

5 'Whoever sows generously will also — generously' *(2 Corinthians 9:6)* (4)

6 Chore (anag.) (5)

10 A great-great-grandson of King Saul *(1 Chronicles 8:35)* (5)

11 One of the 'unclean' things that Jesus said would come out of the human heart *(Matthew 15:19)* (5)

12 'When the — had finished all this tempting, he left him until an opportune time' *(Luke 4:13)* (5)

13 For crushing grapes *(Numbers 18:27)* (9)

14 Go without food *(Luke 18:12)* (4)

15 'He put a new — in my mouth' *(Psalm 40:3)* (4)

18 'Be on guard! Be — ! You do not know when that time will come' *(Mark 13:33)* (5)

20 The Merarites were instructed to camp on this side of the tabernacle *(Numbers 3:35)* (5)

21 Where Sisera and Jabin perished *(Psalm 83:10)* (5)

22 Jesus told Peter he would find one in the mouth of the first fish he caught *(Matthew 17:27)* (4)

23 Clothed *(Nahum 2:3)* (4)

No 79

Across

1 Samson challenged the 30 companions he was given at Timnah with one *(Judges 14:12)* (6)

4 Message *(Numbers 23:18)* (6)

8 'Come to me, all you who are — and burdened, and I will give you rest' *(Matthew 11:28)* (5)

9 A grandson of Benjamin *(1 Chronicles 7:8)* (7)

10 Rebelled *(2 Samuel 14:7)* (5,2)

11 He was the commander of Saul's army *(1 Samuel 14:50)* (5)

12 The jar containing the perfume used to anoint Jesus at Bethany was made of this *(Matthew 26:7)* (9)

17 Last letter of the Greek alphabet *(Revelation 1:8)* (5)

19 'The glory has departed from Israel' *(1 Samuel 4:21)* (7)

21 He was king of Judah for just one year *(2 Kings 8:26)* (7)

22 'May you be blessed by the Lord, the — of heaven and earth' *(Psalm 115:15)* (5)

23 'I have become a byword among them. They — me and keep their distance' *(Job 30:9–10)* (6)

24 Hounds (anag.) (6)

Down

1 'Love your enemies, do good to them... Then your — will be great' *(Luke 6:35)* (6)

2 Israel's lowest lake, known in the Old Testament as the Salt Sea (4,3)

3 'The visions that passed through your mind as you — — your bed are these' *(Daniel 2:28)* (3,2)

5 Remaining part *(2 Kings 19:4)* (7)

6 Comes between Kings and Ezra (abbrev.) (5)

7 Urge *(1 Timothy 5:1)* (6)

9 Priestly son of Maaseiah in the time of Jeremiah *(Jeremiah 29:25)* (9)

13 Trees whose wood was used extensively in the construction of the tabernacle *(Joel 3:18)* (7)

14 Isaac's wife *(Genesis 24:67)* (7)

15 'The Egyptians ill-treated us and made us suffer, putting us — — labour' *(Deuteronomy 26:6)* (2,4)

16 Do, dear (anag.) (6)

18 'Herod called the Magi secretly and found out from them the — time the star had appeared' *(Matthew 2:7)* (5)

20 'Taking the very nature of a servant, being made in — likeness' *(Philippians 2:7)* (5)

No 80

Across

1 'Peter said to him, "Jesus Christ heals you. Get up and — up your mat"' *(Acts 9:34)* (4)

3 Calamity *(Joshua 24:20)* (8)

9 'You did not receive a spirit that makes you a slave again to fear, but you received the Spirit of — ' *(Romans 8:15)* (7)

10 Each without exception *(Luke 3:5)* (5)

11 'The number of men who had — was five thousand' *(Mark 6:44)* (5)

12 'Faith by itself, if it is not accompanied by action, — — ' *(James 2:17)* (2,4)

14 Compiler of the fifth book of the Bible (13)

17 'As his — was, Paul went into the synagogue' *(Acts 17:2)* (6)

19 Writing material *(2 John 12)* (5)
22 'He makes the depths — like a boiling cauldron' *(Job 41:31)* (5)
23 Nose opening *(Amos 4:10)* (7)
24 Steel cat (anag.) (8)
25 'Then I heard the voice of the Lord saying, "Whom shall I — ? And who will go for us?"' *(Isaiah 6:8)* (4)

Down

1 'Uzzah reached out his hand — — the ark, because the oxen stumbled' *(1 Chronicles 13:9)* (2,6)
2 'So you also must be ready, because the Son of Man will come when you — — expect him' *(Matthew 24:44)* (2,3)
4 Some prism tint (anag.) (13)
5 'The star they had seen in the east went — of them until it stopped over the place where the child was' *(Matthew 2:9)* (5)
6 The 'them' referred to in 5 Down *(Matthew 2:7)* (3,4)
7 'May it wait for daylight in vain and not see the first — of dawn' *(Job 3:9)* (4)
8 Opportunity *(Joshua 8:20)* (6)
13 Surprised and frightened *(Luke 1:12)* (8)
15 Out of the ordinary *(Acts 28:2)* (7)
16 Resist strongly *(Acts 11:17)* (6)
18 When Jesus sent out the Twelve, he told them not to take an extra one with them *(Luke 9:3)* (5)
20 'You earn wages, only to put them in a — with holes in it' *(Haggai 1:6)* (5)
21 Eric Liddell, Olympic champion turned missionary, was one (4)

Answers

No 1

ACROSS: 8, Their garments. 9, Pit. 10, Spiritist. 11, Range. 13, End than. 16, Scented. 19, Began. 22, Repayment. 24, Ewe. 25, Such knowledge.

DOWN: 1, Stupor. 2, Beaten. 3, Prospect. 4, Famine. 5, Omri. 6, Enrich. 7, Eshton. 12, Arc. 14, Do battle. 15, Asa. 16, Stress. 17, Expect. 18, Die for. 20, Greedy. 21, Needed. 23, Yoke.

No 2

ACROSS: 1, Bushes. 4, Pisgah. 7, Slow. 8, Abandons. 9, Stockton. 13, Bee. 16, Anglo-Catholic. 17, Its. 19, Scheming. 24, Pleasure. 25, Burn. 26, Useful. 27, Yellow.

DOWN: 1, Best. 2, Shortages. 3, Spark. 4, Piano. 5, Side. 6, Annie. 10, Cross. 11, Teach. 12, Nahum. 13, Bilingual. 14, Each. 15, Dali. 18, Tales. 20, Cruel. 21, Enemy. 22, Half. 23, Snow.

No 3

ACROSS: 1, Accept. 4, Adorns. 8, Curse. 9, Learned. 10, Off beam. 11, Nobel. 12, Livestock. 17, Avail. 19, Ancient. 21, Steward. 22, Abide. 23, Reaper. 24, Height.

DOWN: 1, Anchor. 2, Careful. 3, Piece. 5, Drawn to. 6, R and B. 7, Saddle. 9, Lampstand. 13, Village. 14, Keeping. 15, Caesar. 16, Street. 18, Arena. 20, Cease.

No 4

ACROSS: 1, York. 3, Swearing. 9, Lucifer. 10, Purse. 11, Terah. 12, Obeyed. 14, Demonstration. 17, Impale. 19, Thank. 22, Bahai. 23, Outcast. 24, Dissuade. 25, Less.

DOWN: 1, Yuletide. 2, Recur. 4, Word of the Lord. 5, Ample. 6, Israeli. 7, Glee. 8, Afghan. 13, Anakites. 15, Memphis. 16, Astute. 18, Adieu. 20, Agate. 21, Obed.

No 5

ACROSS: 1, Lawbreakers. 9, Neglect. 10, Reign. 11, Sit. 13, Idly. 16, Abel. 17, Agreed. 18, Hawk. 20, Swim. 21, Advise. 22, Esau. 23, Arts. 25, Bet. 28, Usher. 29, Hittite. 30, Trustworthy.
DOWN: 2, Angel. 3, Bled. 4, Eats. 5, Kurt. 6, Rainbow. 7, Unrighteous. 8, Unblemished. 12, Irenic. 14, Yak. 15, Grudge. 19, Weather. 20, Sea. 24, Reith. 25, Bros. 26, Thaw. 27, Stir.

No 6

ACROSS: 1, Conscience. 7, Arrival. 8, Yours. 10, Tidy. 11, Restrain. 13, Quaker. 15, Gateau. 17, Athenian. 18, Amen. 21, Eliot. 22, Enables. 23, Impressive.
DOWN: 1, Cured. 2, Nave. 3, Calver. 4, Egyptian. 5, Courage. 6, Earthquake. 9, Sinfulness. 12, Leinster. 14, Atheism. 16, Waters. 19, Milne. 20, Taxi.

No 7

ACROSS: 1, Care. 3, Paradise. 8, Null. 9, Profaned. 11, Legalistic. 14, Closed. 15, Stores. 17, Missionary. 20, Covenant. 21, Thai. 22, Trade-off. 23, Eden.
DOWN: 1, Conflict. 2, Religion. 4, Arrest. 5, Affliction. 6, Iona. 7, Eddy. 10, Allegiance. 12, Preached. 13, Assyrian. 16, A son of. 18, Scot. 19, DVLA.

No 8

ACROSS: 8. Assyriologist. 9, Sue. 10, Innocence. 11, Motif. 13, Defrock. 16, Attalia. 19, Lord's. 22, Prophetic. 24, Mac. 25, Contraception.
DOWN: 1, Ransom. 2, Ascent. 3, Fruitful. 4, Joined. 5, BOAC. 6, Sign to. 7, Streak. 12, Out. 14, Full cups. 15, Cud. 16, Alpaca. 17, Thorns. 18, Attack. 20, Remain. 21, Second. 23, Hurt.

No 9

ACROSS: 1. Mosaic. 4, Scales. 7, Cana. 8, Claudius. 9, Sadducee. 13, SLM. 16, Self-confident. 17, Sad. 19, Radiuses. 24, Shepherd. 25, Bind. 26, Astern. 27, Arthur.

DOWN: 1, Mock. 2, Sandalled. 3, CICCU. 4, Share. 5, Aide. 6, Equal. 10, Decor. 11, Caned. 12, Elihu. 13, Sherebiah. 14, Moth. 15, Uses. 18, Ashes. 20, ASEAN. 21, India. 22, Apse. 23, Eder.

No 10

ACROSS: 1, Access. 4, Blinds. 8, Rhyme. 9, Loyalty. 10, Antwerp. 11, Aenon. 12, Loftiness. 17, Satan. 19, Obadiah. 21, On earth. 22, Storm. 23, Exhale. 24, Depths.

DOWN: 1, Adrian. 2, Crystal. 3, Siege. 5, Lay bare. 6, Nylon. 7, Saying. 9, Lappidoth. 13, Funeral. 14, Spit out. 15, Ashore. 16, Thomas. 18, Teeth. 20, Aisle.

No 11

ACROSS: 1. Dare. 3, Cherubim. 9, Son Tohu. 10, Yield. 11, Ranch. 12, Enlist. 14, Baalah of Judah. 17, Edward. 19, Sheol. 22, Media. 23, Open air. 24, Apostasy. 25, Eton.

DOWN: 1, Describe. 2, Run in. 4, Household gods. 5, Royal. 6, Blessed. 7, MIDI. 8, Joshua. 13, Children. 15, Added to. 16, Jasper. 18, Await. 20, Exalt. 21, YMCA.

No 12

ACROSS: 1, Hopefulness. 9, Hitting. 10, du Pre. 11, Ere. 13, Ozni. 16. Wait. 17, Climbs. 18, Obey. 20, Joni. 21, Cuckoo. 22, In it. 23, Yaws. 25, Elm. 28, Alarm. 29, Epistle. 30, Whitsuntide.

DOWN: 2, Often. 3, Exit. 4, Urge. 5, Node. 6, Soprano. 7, Theological. 8, Westminster. 12, Rebuke. 14, Icy. 15, Ritual. 19, Epitaph. 20, Joy. 24, Acted. 25, Emit. 26, Menu. 27, Gift.

No 13

ACROSS: 1, Tabernacle. 7, Absalom. 8, Incas. 10, Roes. 11, Captured. 13, Fright. 15, Cavell. 17, Cyclonic. 18, Herb. 21, Sonar. 22, Amazing. 23, Settlement.
DOWN: 1, Taste. 2, Bold. 3, Ramiah. 4, Abiathar. 5, Lucerne. 6, Sacrifices. 9, Saddlebags. 12, Theocrat. 14, Incense. 16, Pilate. 19, Exist. 20, Save.

No 14

ACROSS: 1, Cock. 3, Shackles. 8, Play. 9, Paradise. 11, Faithfully. 14, Enmesh. 15, Unseen. 17, Armageddon. 20, Benjamin. 21, Beri. 22, Capitals. 23, USPG.
DOWN: 1, Cup of tea. 2, Charisma. 4, Heap up. 5, Challenged. 6, Lois. 7, Slew. 10, The Servant. 12, Lewdness. 13, Unending. 16, Daniel. 18, BBFC. 19, Snap.

No 15

ACROSS: 8, Cross-examined. 9, Ash. 10, Apocrypha. 11, Sci-fi. 13, Typical. 16, Visited. 19, Offer. 22, No account. 24, RAC. 25, Sovereign Lord.
DOWN: 1, Oceans. 2, Hophni. 3, Islamist. 4, Exhort. 5, Omar. 6, On spec. 7, Add all. 12, CBI. 14, Plotting. 15, Awe. 16, Vanish. 17, Starve. 18, Daub it. 20, Furrow. 21, Recede. 23, Cure.

No 16

ACROSS: 1, Planet. 4, Rugged. 7, True. 8, Augustus. 9, Attitude. 13, Bed. 16, Participation. 17, War. 19, Hillside. 24, Baldhead. 25, Bede. 26, Census. 27, Arisen.
DOWN: 1, Path. 2, Adulterer. 3, Tract. 4, Rigid. 5, Gust. 6, Exude. 10, Irish. 11, Uriel. 12, Esau's. 13, Blindness. 14, Deny. 15, Spew. 18, Awake. 20, Ideas. 21, Lydia. 22, Odes. 23, Lean.

No 17

ACROSS: 1, Cosmic. 4, Thomas. 8, In his. 9, Delaiah. 10, Falwell. 11, Water. 12, Recovered. 17, Sidon. 19, Radiant. 21, Centaur. 22, Broil. 23, Eleven. 24, Prison.
DOWN: 1, Cliffs. 2, Scholar. 3, Issue. 5, Holy war. 6, Moist. 7, Sphere. 9, Deliverer. 13, Candace. 14, Deacons. 15, Psyche. 16, Stolen. 18, Dance. 20, Debar.

No 18

ACROSS: 1, Stop. 3, Call upon. 9, Regular. 10, Octet. 11, Inner. 12, Hudson. 14, Holy Communion. 17, Myself. 19, See to. 22, About. 23, Iterate. 24, Monarchy. 25, Stet.
DOWN: 1, Straight. 2, Organ. 4, Abraham's faith. 5, Lloyd. 6, Puteoli. 7, Note. 8, Cleric. 13, Innocent. 15, Lay down. 16, Ussher. 18, Enter. 20, Enact. 21, Balm.

No 19

ACROSS: 1, Sabachthani. 9, Ephraim. 10, Patch. 11, Eve. 13, Farm. 16, Limp. 17, Rachel. 18, OHMS. 20, I die. 21, Simeon. 22, Task. 23, Nard. 25, See. 28, Onion. 29, Worries. 30, Shipwrecked.
DOWN: 2, Asher. 3, Adam. 4, Home. 5, Hope. 6, Not find. 7, Self-control. 8, Shepherdess. 12, Viewed. 14, Mrs. 15, Scribe. 19, Messiah. 20, Inn. 24, Alive. 25, Snip. 26, Ewer. 27, Eric.

No 20

ACROSS: 1, Sabbatical. 7, Opinion. 8, Laing. 10, Olga. 11, Galilean. 13, Sardis. 15, Severe. 17, Adultery. 18, Flea. 21, Swazi. 22, Acetate. 23, Revelation.
DOWN: 1, Sling. 2, Brim. 3, Annual. 4, Ill-timed. 5, Abilene. 6, Colossians. 9, Gennesaret. 12, Diatribe. 14, Roulade. 16, Errata. 19, Learn. 20, Levi.

No 21

ACROSS: 1, John. 3, And James. 8, Near. 9, Omission. 11, Theocratic. 14, Asleep. 15, By-path. 17, Stalingrad. 20, Backbone. 21, Baca. 22, Whose eye. 23, Seth.

DOWN: 1, Jonathan. 2, Heavenly. 4, No meat. 5, Justifying. 6, Maid. 7, Sins. 10, Acceptable. 12, Marriage. 13, Shadrach. 16, Plenty. 18, A bow. 19, ECHO.

No 22

ACROSS: 8, Kiriath Jearim. 9, Toe. 10, Ill at ease. 11, Hated. 13, Miletus. 16, Started. 19, Micah. 22, Leviticus. 24, Eli. 25, Mary and Joseph.

DOWN: 1, Sketch. 2, Priest. 3, Samizdat. 4, Shalom. 5, Wept. 6, Breast. 7, Embers. 12, Art. 14, Limassol. 15, UNA. 16, Salome. 17, Adverb. 18, Decade. 20, Clever. 21, Height. 23, Tear.

No 23

ACROSS: 1, Deacon. 4, Appear. 7, Wits. 8, Heavenly. 9, Argument. 13, Mob. 16, Broken-hearted. 17, Ran. 19, Suddenly. 24, Obstacle. 25, John. 26, Enable. 27, Market.

DOWN: 1, Dawn. 2, Afternoon. 3, Nehum. 4, Again. 5, Prey. 6, All to. 10, Users. 11, Ephod. 12, Trace. 13, Metalwork. 14, Body. 15, Eber. 18, Alban. 20, Uncle. 21, Dream. 22, Stab. 23, Gnat.

No 24

ACROSS: 1, Thanks. 4, Banner. 8, Esher. 9, Azariah. 10, Compare. 11, Ishma. 12, Doorposts. 17, Oaths. 19, Galatia. 21, Papyrus. 22, Frail. 23, Listen. 24, Hyssop.

DOWN: 1, Trench. 2, Ashamed. 3, Karma. 5, Ananias. 6, Neigh. 7, Reheat. 9, Areopagus. 13, Observe. 14, Satraps. 15, Compel. 16, Gallop. 18, Tapes. 20, Lofty.

No 25

ACROSS: 1, Hide. 3, Disgrace. 9, Sonship. 10, Oaths. 11, Tutti. 12, Ignore. 14, Foreknowledge. 17, Ashram. 19, Men or. 22, Aroma. 23, Nineveh. 24, Amethyst. 25, Trod.
DOWN: 1, His staff. 2, Do not. 4, Imprisonments. 5, Groan. 6, Altered. 7, Easy. 8, Shrink. 13, Searched. 15, Restore. 16, Lament. 18, Reach. 20, Never. 21, Jada.

No 26

ACROSS: 1, Godlessness. 9, Egotism. 10, After. 11, Eat. 13, Sort. 16, Plan. 17, Escape. 18, Odds. 20, Idem. 21, No fear. 22, Idle. 23, Abet. 25, Ail. 28, Eaves. 29, Achieve. 30, Grasshopper.
DOWN: 2, Odour. 3, Lair. 4, Same. 5, Neat. 6, Settled. 7, Gershonites. 8, Grandmother. 12, Apples. 14, TES. 15, Octopi. 19, Deliver. 20, Ira. 24, Breve. 25, As is. 26, Lash. 27, Whip.

No 27

ACROSS: 1, Prosperity. 7, Raisins. 8, Admit. 10, View. 11, Confetti. 13, Distil. 15, Groyne. 17, Navigate. 18, Whit. 21, Enoch. 22, Trodden. 23, Prophetess.
DOWN: 1, Pride. 2, Ovid. 3, Pastor. 4, Reaffirm. 5, Timothy. 6, Providence. 9, Tridentine. 12, Kingship. 14, Saviour. 16, Statue. 19, Hades. 20, Rome.

No 28

ACROSS: 1, Wine. 3, The alert. 8, Ooze. 9, Passover. 11, Garden Tomb. 14, Cannot. 15, Elisha. 17, Gethsemane. 20, Own house. 21, Lisa. 22, Flogging. 23, Stye.
DOWN: 1, Wrong act. 2, Nazarene. 4, Health. 5, Assemblies. 6, Envy. 7, Turn. 10, Before long. 12, Iscariot. 13, Take care. 16, The Son. 18, Loaf. 19, Unto.

No 29

ACROSS: 8, Transgressors. 9, Out. 10, Ephesians. 11, Throb. 13, Ramadan. 16, Nearest. 19, Neath. 22, Childless. 24, Ant. 25, Excommunicate.

DOWN: 1, Utmost. 2, Easter. 3, Assemble. 4, Archer. 5, Isis. 6, To hand. 7, As a son. 12, Hoe. 14, Monastic. 15, Apt. 16, Nuclei. 17, A piece. 18, Tied up. 20, Ararat. 21, Hatred. 23, Dome.

No 30

ACROSS: 1, Debtor. 4, Shaken. 7, Ache. 8, Leavened. 9, Overcome. 13, Etc. 16, Troublemaking. 17, Par. 19, Ignatius. 24, Treasure. 25, Mene. 26, Astray. 27, Dinner.

DOWN: 1, Deaf. 2, Behaviour. 3, Relic. 4, Swarm. 5, Aged. 6, Elect. 10, Rabbi. 11, Ocean. 12, Exalt. 13, Epicurean. 14, Cage. 15, Step. 18, Acres. 20, Gaudy. 21, An end. 22, Fair. 23, Fear.

No 31

ACROSS: 1, Ambush. 4, School. 8, Tired. 9, Famines. 10, Citadel. 11, Endor. 12, Atonement. 17, Avert. 19, Oracles. 21, Married. 22, Lance. 23, Rhythm. 24, Hyssop.

DOWN: 1, Attach. 2, Biretta. 3, Sided. 5, Compete. 6, Owned. 7, Lustre. 9, Falsehood. 13, Ostrich. 14, Talents. 15, Farmer. 16, Asleep. 18, Early. 20, Alley.

No 32

ACROSS: 1, Dove. 3, Offender. 9, Alcohol. 10, Loses. 11, Horam. 12, Ophrah. 14, Archbishopric. 17, Samuel. 19, Dwarf. 22, Lacks. 23, Imagine. 24, Military. 25, Revd.

DOWN: 1, Drachmas. 2, Vicar. 4, Fellow-soldier. 5, Eglah. 6, Despair. 7, Rust. 8, The mob. 13, Scofield. 15, Chancel. 16, Ordeal. 18, Upset. 20, Alike. 21, Elim.

No 33

ACROSS: 1, Charioteers. 9, Immoral. 10, Cairo. 11, SAE. 13, Inns. 16, Firm. 17, Accuse. 18, East. 20, Ogam. 21, Judith. 22, Seba. 23, Msgr. 25, Den. 28, Inane. 29, Entreat. 30, Chrysoprase.
DOWN: 2, Human. 3, Rare. 4, Oils. 5, Ecce. 6, Raising. 7, Citizenship. 8, Commemorate. 12, Assail. 14, Sat. 15, Scouse. 19, Sabbath. 20, Ohm. 24, Seeds. 25, Deny. 26, Nero. 27, Star.

No 34

ACROSS: 1, Foreigners. 7, Accepts. 8, Pilot. 10, Toss. 11, Knitwear. 13, Foment. 15, Came to. 17, Lighting. 18, Nisi. 21, Yearn. 22, Worn-out. 23, Fatherless.
DOWN: 1, Facts. 2, Ripe. 3, Insane. 4, Nephtoah. 5, Relieve. 6, Faithfully. 9, Terrorists. 12, One tenth. 14, Magdala. 16, Answer. 19, Irons. 20, Tree.

No 35

ACROSS: 1, Soco. 3, Criminal. 8, Nard. 9, Laughter. 11, Ezion Geber. 14, Coggan. 15, Millet. 17, Blind guide. 20, Hymnbook. 21, Cast. 22, Wesleyan. 23, Glad.
DOWN: 1, Sentence. 2, Carriage. 4, Reader. 5, Muggeridge. 6, Note. 7, Lord. 10, Infallible. 12, All in all. 13, Attested. 16, Angola. 18, Show. 19, Amos.

No 36

ACROSS: 8, Indescribable. 9, Two. 10, Lying lips. 11, Ennui. 13, Greater. 16, Wrestle. 19, Image. 22, Loincloth. 24, Ebb. 25, Intentionally.
DOWN: 1, Little. 2, Adjoin. 3, Psalmist. 4, Crying. 5, A big. 6, Oboist. 7, Censer. 12, Nor. 14, Epiphany. 15, Egg. 16, Welkin. 17, Exists. 18, Euodia. 20, Age-old. 21, Embryo. 23, Cana.

No 37

ACROSS: 1, Depend. 4, Canopy. 7, Beak. 8, Irritate. 9, Zedekiah. 13, Ate. 16, Job's comforter. 17, NAE. 19, Lang Syne. 24, Blockade. 25, Five. 26, Enigma. 27, Drench.
DOWN: 1, Debt. 2, Peaceable. 3, Drink. 4, Curia. 5, Nuts. 6, Put it. 10, Excel. 11, Is man. 12, Hoofs. 13, Attention. 14, Ezra. 15, Ijon. 18, Aslan. 20, Abana. 21, Greed. 22, GCMG. 23, Leah.

No 38

ACROSS: 1, Armour. 4, Twelve. 8, Ulric. 9, Imitate. 10, Lectern. 11, Trees. 12, Endurance. 17, Harem. 19, Newborn. 21, Divorce. 22, Erica. 23, Wisest. 24, Stoned.
DOWN: 1, Aquila. 2, Miracle. 3, Uncle. 5, Written. 6, Leave. 7, Ever so. 9, Ignorance. 13, Damaris. 14, Erosion. 15, Shadow. 16, Onward. 18, Raves. 20, Wheat.

No 39

ACROSS: 1, Wage. 3, Cleansed. 9, Plateau. 10, Ready. 11, Did so. 12, Hollow. 14, Unregenerated. 17, Offers. 19, Islam. 22, Is not. 23, Overran. 24, Barracks. 25, Legs.
DOWN: 1, Wiped out. 2, Guard. 4, Laughing-stock. 5, April. 6, Seaport. 7, Days. 8, Belong. 13, Oddments. 15, Refiner. 16, Raided. 18, Extra. 20, Large. 21, Limb.

No 40

ACROSS: 1, Corinthians. 9, Abandon. 10, Eglon. 11, Spa. 13, Deem. 16, Hi-fi. 17, Abijah. 18, Ohad. 20, Myth. 21, Now see. 22, Knit. 23, Tide. 25, Arm. 28, Nahor. 29, All done. 30, Kind-hearted.
DOWN: 2, Of age. 3, ISDN. 4, Tens. 5, Idea. 6, Nullify. 7, Hardworking. 8, Enlightened. 12, Praise. 14, Mad. 15, Vigour. 19, Abishai. 20, Met. 24, Is one. 25, Arid. 26, Male. 27, Slur.

No 41

ACROSS: 1, Priesthood. 7, Replica. 8, Get up. 10, Calf. 11, Governor. 13, See you. 15, Not see. 17, Incident. 18, Sake. 21, NSPCC. 22, Trample. 23, Perishable.
DOWN: 1, Papal. 2, In it. 3, Shalom. 4, Huguenot. 5, Outings. 6, Procession. 9, Perseveres. 12, Mordecai. 14, Escapee. 16, Snatch. 19, Apple. 20, Lamb.

No 42

ACROSS: 1, Baby. 3, Stimulus. 8, Liar. 9, Forsaken. 11, Episcopacy. 14, Eagles. 15, Clergy. 17, Strengthen. 20, Holiness. 21, Obed. 22, Bethesda. 23, Stay.
DOWN: 1, Believer. 2, Beatings. 4, Troops. 5, Musicology. 6, Like. 7, Sent. 10, Acceptance. 12, Prohibit. 13, Dying day. 16, Sensed. 18, Ahab. 19, Blot.

No 43

ACROSS: 4, Grandchildren. 9, Pro. 10, Marvelled. 11, Strut. 13, Startle. 16, Babysit. 19, Orate. 22, Eucharist. 24, Map. 25, Commissioners.
DOWN: 1, Egypt's. 2, Favour. 3, Edomites. 4, Thorns. 5, Blue. 6, Armlet. 7, On edge. 12, Tea. 14, Adoption. 15, Lot. 16, Breach. 17, Become. 18, This So. 20, Armies. 21, Expose. 23, Avid.

No 44

ACROSS: 1, Riches. 4, Abner's. 7, Soul. 8, Damascus. 9, Statutes. 13, Add. 16, Craftsmanship. 17, Old. 19, Redeemer. 24, Walls are. 25, Wise. 26, Target. 27, Thieve.
DOWN: 1, Rest. 2, Courtyard. 3, Sadhu. 4, Arm he. 5, Nose. 6, Round. 10, Tutor. 11, Timid. 12, Sense. 13, Ashbelite. 14, Dips. 15, Echo. 18, Lhasa. 20, Exact. 21, Erect. 22, Flog. 23, Mede.

No 45

ACROSS: 1, Amazed. 4, Others. 8, Peter. 9, Zebedee. 10, Accuser. 11, Endue. 12, Scripture. 17, Shrub. 19, Abashed. 21, Foolish. 22, Upset. 23, Loathe. 24, Lesser.
DOWN: 1, Appeal. 2, Attacks. 3, Earns. 5, Tableau. 6, Ended. 7, Shekel. 9, Zarephath. 13, Rubbish. 14, Ephesus. 15, Useful. 16, Editor. 18, Rhoda. 20, Abuse.

No 46

ACROSS: 1, Also. 3, Offering. 9, The Magi. 10, Rules. 11, Soper. 12, Help me. 14, Isaac and Jacob. 17, Scorch. 19, In man. 22, Loads. 23, Inertia. 24, Vicinity. 25, Belt.
DOWN: 1, Artistic. 2, Sleep. 4, Faith in Christ. 5, Enrol. 6, Islamic. 7, Gasp. 8, Fabric. 13, Abundant. 15, Archaic. 16, Jailer. 18, Resin. 20, Mitre. 21, Slav.

No 47

ACROSS: 1. Bartholomew. 9, Evil one. 10, Adore. 11, Ran. 13, Oreb. 16, Zinc. 17, Entail. 18, Hung. 20, Lehi. 21, Joshua. 22, Pity. 23, Wide. 25, Age. 28, Alarm. 29, Partake. 30, Sennacherib.
DOWN: 2, Alive. 3, Took. 4, Over. 5, Onan. 6, Emotive. 7, Jehoshaphat. 8, Melchizedek. 12, A light. 14, Beg. 15, Strong. 19, Not have. 20, Law. 24, Iraqi. 25, Amen. 26, Epic. 27, Free.

No 48

ACROSS: 1, Jehoiachin. 7, Endured. 8, Eased. 10, Rash. 11, Startled. 13, Easier. 15, Rubric. 17, Impurity. 18, Feet. 21, Eye at. 22, Ready to. 23, Holy Spirit.
DOWN: 1, Judas. 2, Harm. 3, Is duty. 4, Cheerful. 5, Insular. 6, Jezreelite. 9, Dedication. 12, Secretly. 14, Supremo. 16, Stir up. 19. Egypt. 20, Hair.

No 49

ACROSS: 1, Lame. 3, Obtained. 8, Omit. 9, Merchant. 11, Burdensome. 14, Crafty. 15, Please. 17, Blacksmith. 20, Splendid. 21, Tier. 22, Singeing. 23, Hand.
DOWN: 1, Look back. 2, Main road. 4, Breast. 5, Accomplish. 6, Near. 7, Date. 10, Pestilence. 12, Basilica. 13, Tethered. 16, Action. 18, Asa's. 19, Clan.

No 50

ACROSS: 8, Bottomless pit. 9, Ice. 10, Decalogue. 11, Limbo. 13, Seconds. 16, Crimson. 19, Eager. 22, Abhorrent. 24, Lap. 25, Alpha and Omega.
DOWN: 1, Abdiel. 2, Stream. 3, Wondrous. 4, Flocks. 5, USCL. 6, A pagan. 7, Athens. 12, IOR. 14, Creation. 15, Dye. 16, Cravat. 17, In hope. 18, Need no. 20, Galley. 21, Repeat. 23, Read.

No 51

ACROSS: 1, Credit. 4, Tackle. 7, Cain. 8, Kenaniah. 9, Strength. 13, Beg. 16, Salvation Army. 17, ARC. 19, Every day. 24, Admonish. 25, Dire. 26, Sneeze. 27, Bronze.
DOWN: 1, Cock. 2, Epistolic. 3, Taken. 4, Tenet. 5, Cane. 6, Leave. 10, Erase. 11, Guide. 12, Honey. 13, Barbarian. 14, Guys. 15, Asia. 18, Rod in. 20, Voice. 21, Rahab. 22, Hope. 23, Mene.

No 52

ACROSS: 1, Awaken. 4, Quench. 8, Hit me. 9, Sadness. 10, Semitic. 11, Ridge. 12, Testimony. 17, Psalm. 19, Indulge. 21, Deserve. 22, Ariel. 23, Rose as. 24, Beggar.
DOWN: 1, Aghast. 2, Attempt. 3, Eject. 5, Undergo. 6, No end. 7, Hasten. 9, Sacrifice. 13, Samaria. 14, Yelling. 15, Spider. 16, Dealer. 18, Asses. 20, Drake.

No 53

ACROSS: 1, Womb. 3, Agnostic. 9, Long ago. 10, Fleet. 11, Horeb. 12, Yellow. 14, Deceitfulness. 17, Banish. 19, Towel. 22, Boils. 23, Inferno. 24, Eternity. 25, Defy.
DOWN: 1, Will hide. 2, Minor. 4, Glory of Christ. 5, Offal. 6, The Robe. 7, City. 8, Zabbai. 13, Psalmody. 15, Chalice. 16, Let off. 18, If son. 20, Worse. 21, Able.

No 54

ACROSS: 1, Overwhelmed. 9, Valleys. 10, Strap. 11, Top. 13, Reel. 16, To do. 17, Incite. 18, Load. 20, West. 21, Notice. 22, Wash. 23, Thin. 25, Ash. 28, Noah's. 29, Ever not. 30, Onesiphorus.
DOWN: 2, Value. 3, Reed. 4, Host. 5, Lisp. 6, Ear lobe. 7, Overflowing. 8, Opportunity. 12, Obtain. 14, Lid. 15, A cross. 19, Abstain. 20, Wet. 24, Hindu. 25, Asks. 26, Help. 27, Hero.

No 55

ACROSS: 1, Wickedness. 7, Harpist. 8, Teach. 10, Side. 11, Impostor. 13, Encamp. 15, Saddle. 17, Ignorant. 18, Tent. 21, Grass. 22, Olivier. 23, Wrongdoers.
DOWN: 1, World. 2, Crib. 3, Entomb. 4, National. 5, Started. 6, Whispering. 9, Harvesters. 12, Imprison. 14, Centaur. 16, Unload. 19, Evils, 20, Give.

No 56

ACROSS: 1, Wife. 3, To battle. 8, Obal. 9, Disciple. 11, Bitterness. 14, Niacin. 15, Attain. 17, Passionate. 20, Tertiary. 21, Meet. 22, Weakness. 23, Deer.
DOWN: 1, Woodbine. 2, Feast day. 4, Orient. 5, Accusation. 6, Type. 7, Eyes. 10, Dedication. 12, Gadarene. 13, Ancestor. 16, Esdras. 18, Stew. 19, Area.

No 57

ACROSS: 8, Prince of Peace. 9, INF. 10, Unmarried. 11, Gulag. 13, Treason. 16, In aid of. 19, Arena. 22, Calvinist. 24, Pad. 25, Moses and Aaron.

DOWN: 1, Spring. 2, Sinful. 3, Scourged. 4, Commit. 5, Spur. 6, Matins. 7, Feed on. 12, Urn. 14, Erastian, 15, Own. 16, Income. 17, At last. 18, Friend. 20, Empire. 21, Adding. 23, Inst.

No 58

ACROSS: 1, Labour. 4, Autumn. 7, Stay. 8, Darkness. 9, Reasoned. 13, Act. 16, Presbyterians. 17, Sat. 19, Ridicule. 24, Reproach. 25, Abib. 26, Celtic. 27, Intend.

DOWN: 1, Lose. 2, Blame rest. 3, Radio. 4, Agree. 5, Tend. 6, Music. 10, Sober. 11, Noted. 12, Doric. 13, Available. 14, Test. 15, Apes. 18, As Eve. 20, Isaac. 21, Ishvi. 22, Fret. 23, Ebed.

No 59

ACROSS: 1, Lawyer. 4, Balsam. 8, Caleb. 9, Jehoram. 10, Sparrow. 11, Exile. 12, Excellent. 17, Act in. 19, Endemic. 21, Slavery. 22, Galal. 23, Silent. 24, Tarsus.

DOWN: 1, Locust. 2, Welfare. 3, Ember. 5, Athlete. 6, Sarai. 7, Member. 9, Jewellery. 13, Condemn. 14, Temples. 15, Causes. 16, Scales. 18, Trail. 20, Dogma.

No 60

ACROSS: 1, Into. 3, Christen. 9; Saw Jehu. 10, Names. 11, Rinse. 12, Entail. 14, Bread of angels. 17, Adorns. 19, Table. 22, Leech. 23, Account. 24, Assemble. 25, Deed.

DOWN: 1, Inscribe. 2, To win. 4, House of Israel. 5, If not. 6, Timnite. 7, Nash. 8, Defend. 13, Asserted. 15, Endless. 16, Notice. 18, Raham. 20, Brute. 21, Plea.

No 61

ACROSS: 1, Instruction. 9, Newborn. 10, Storm. 11, Ink. 13, East. 16, Silo. 17, Abound. 18, Ibex. 20, A bit. 21, Unfair. 22, Abba. 23, Ebal. 25, Bar. 28, Curse. 29, Upright. 30, Commandment.
DOWN: 2, Now is. 3, Tool. 4, Unni. 5, Task. 6, Oholiab. 7, Inheritance. 8, Immortality. 12, Ninian. 14, Tax. 15, Joanna. 19, Embargo. 20, Are. 24, Began. 25, Beam. 26, Ruin. 27, Aram.

No 62

ACROSS: 1, Michaelmas. 7, Trumpet. 8, Zadok. 10, Rank. 11, Mount Hor. 13, Acacia. 15, Ask not. 17, Ebenezer. 18, Thai. 21, Sigma. 22, Is a tree. 23, Bridegroom.
DOWN: 1, Mourn. 2, Cups. 3, Author. 4, Laziness. 5, And when. 6, Stargazers. 9, Kerethites. 12, Vineyard. 14, Avenger. 16, Seeing. 19, Harem. 20, Hazo.

No 63

ACROSS: 1, Flax. 3, Approach. 8, Raid. 9, Teaching. 11, Wanderings. 14, Let out. 15, Dimmer. 17, Flattering. 20, Advocate. 21, Diet. 22, Balances. 23, Aner.
DOWN: 1, Farewell. 2, Alienate. 4, Poetic. 5, Recognised. 6, Amid. 7, High. 10, Republican. 12, Ambition. 13, Brighter. 16, Statue. 18, SATB. 19, Evil.

No 64

ACROSS: 8, Tax collectors. 9, End. 10, Desperate. 11, Music. 13, Accused. 16, Willing. 19, Named. 22, Divisible. 24, Apt. 25, Water-carriers.
DOWN: 1, Stream. 2, Exodus. 3, Mordecai. 4, Elisha. 5, Acre. 6, Romans. 7, Ascend. 12, Uri. 14, Can learn. 15, Eye. 16, Widows. 17, Levite. 18, Gibeah. 20, Moaned. 21, Detest. 23, Sure.

No 65

ACROSS: 1, Cubits. 4, Summer. 7, Rain. 8, Needless. 9, Adoniram. 13, CMJ. 16, Green pastures. 17, Yes. 19, Homilies. 24, Hitherto. 25, Stab. 26, Strain. 27, Energy.
DOWN: Care. 2, Blindness. 3, Sunni. 4, Sheba. 5, Mile. 6, Epsom. 10, Ninth. 11, Realm. 12, Metal. 13, Carpenter. 14, Just. 15, Ugly. 18, Edict. 20, Ocran. 21, I hope. 22, Shia. 23, Obey.

No 66

ACROSS: 1, Bodies. 4, Spoken. 8, Agent. 9, Fervent. 10, Tympani. 11, Bulls. 12, Daughters. 17, Cloak. 19, Elkanah. 21, Encamps. 22, Omega. 23, Turn to. 24, Ascent.
DOWN: 1, Beauty. 2, Dreamed. 3, Extra. 5, Parable. 6, Kneel. 7, Not ask. 9, Faithless. 13, Unkempt. 14, Sincere. 15, Accent. 16, Thwart. 18, Occur. 20, Knows.

No 67

ACROSS: 1, Meal. 3, Splendid. 9, Regular. 10, Us new. 11, Greed. 12, Impure. 14, The meditation. 17, Teresa. 19, Renew. 22, Ditto. 23, Invader. 24, Merchant. 25, A bed.
DOWN: 1, My rights. 2, Argue. 4, Participation. 5, Equip. 6, Denarii. 7, Dawn. 8, Pledge. 13, Answered. 15, Elector. 16, Arrive. 18, Enoch. 20, Nadab. 21, Adam.

No 68

ACROSS: 1, Foolishness. 9, Entrust. 10, Local. 11, Eve. 13, Ears. 16, Coax. 17, Afraid. 18, Ruby. 20, Shun. 21, Came to. 22, Tops. 23, Near. 25, Sew. 28, Olive. 29, Abagtha. 30, Ambassadors.
DOWN: 2, Outer. 3, Loud. 4, Site. 5, Nile. 6, Succoth. 7, Celebration. 8, Alexandrian. 12, Veiled. 14, Say. 15, Create. 19, Baptism. 20, Son. 24, Enter. 25, Set a. 26, Ways. 27, Sand.

No 69

ACROSS: 1, Directions. 7, In error. 8, Outed. 10, Fold. 11, Denarius. 13, Cloths. 15, Bengal. 17, Listened. 18, Spot. 21, Young. 22, Voice to. 23, Celebrated.
DOWN: 1, Dwell. 2, Rare. 3, Cursed. 4, Idolater. 5, Nothing. 6, Difficulty. 9, Desolation. 12, The eagle. 14, Obscure. 16, Weaver. 19, Plead. 20, Gift.

No 70

ACROSS: 1, Joab. 3, All Souls. 8, Ball. 9, Evermore. 11, Sacrificed. 14, To take. 15, Please. 17, Sensuality. 20, Decision. 21, Hero. 22, East side. 23, Used.
DOWN: 1, Jebusite. 2, Allocate. 4, Love is. 5, Serve altar. 6, Upon. 7, Seed. 10, Sicknesses. 12, Laziness. 13, Very good. 16, As bold. 18, Edge. 19, Acts.

No 71

ACROSS: 8, Granddaughter. 9, Own. 10, Latter-day. 11, Dealt. 13, Soprano. 16, Delayed. 19, Reeds. 22, Patriarch. 24, Ira. 25, Rowan Williams.
DOWN: 1, Age-old. 2, Narnia. 3, Idolatry. 4, Dante's. 5, Agee. 6, Stadia. 7, Pray to. 12, Eye. 14, Porthole. 15, Nod. 16, Depart. 17, Lot two. 18, Darwin. 20, Elijah. 21, Sparse. 23, Iona.

No 72

ACROSS: 1, Jeered. 4, Church. 7, Hire. 8, Onesimus. 9, Blessing. 13, She. 16, Sheep-shearing. 17, Kit. 19, Reigning. 24, Boasting. 25, Firm. 26, Essene. 27, Nectar.
DOWN: 1, Jehu. 2, Enrolment. 3, Dross. 4, Clean. 5, Unit. 6, Crush. 10, Super. 11, Ithai. 12, Grain. 13, Scientist. 14, Eggs. 15, Esek. 18, Idols. 20, Elite. 21, Gog on. 22, Isle. 23, Omer.

No 73

ACROSS: 1, Our cry. 4, Aghast. 8, Thumb. 9, Browses. 10, In doing. 11, Tithe. 12, Phoenicia. 17, Haste. 19, Implore. 21, Warning. 22, After. 23, Design. 24, Fleece.

DOWN: 1, Obtain. 2, Round up. 3, Rabbi. 5, Gnostic. 6, Asset. 7, Tasted. 9, Beginning. 13, Opening. 14, Apostle. 15, Showed. 16, Decree. 18, Sores. 20, Pearl.

No 74

ACROSS: 1, Onam. 3, Harmed in. 9, Emperor. 10, Noses. 11, Clasp. 12, Maacah. 14, Moses and Aaron. 17, Avoids. 19, Cabul. 22, Above. 23, Rioting. 24, Christ in. 25, Test.

DOWN: 1, Overcome. 2, Alpha. 4, Abram and Sarai. 5, Manna. 6, Despair. 7, Nest. 8, Grapes. 13, And light. 15, Saviour. 16, Anchor. 18, Ideas. 20, Bribe. 21, MARC.

No 75

ACROSS: 1, Vindication. 9, Ishmael. 10, Where. 11, Man. 13, Heir. 16, It so. 17, Unites. 18, Race. 20, Leah. 21, At ease. 22, Sups. 23, Trap. 25, Set. 28, Trust. 29, Hosanna. 30, Secretaries.

DOWN: 2, Ishvi. 3, Draw. 4, Calm. 5, Town. 6, Open the. 7, Kir Hareseth. 8, Jehoshaphat. 12, Aretas. 14, Rue. 15, Little. 19, Capture. 20, Let. 24, Range. 25, Stir. 26, That. 27, User.

No 76

ACROSS: 1, Calamities. 7, Assured. 8, Perch. 10, Akim. 11, Be mother. 13, Nearly. 15, Sign be. 17, Twilight. 18, Shut. 21, Stain. 22, Ramadan. 23, Assemblies.

DOWN: 1, Cushi. 2, Lyre. 3, Madmen. 4, To profit. 5, Earthen. 6, Canaanites. 9, Harvesting. 12, Alliance. 14, Animals. 16, Cherub. 19, Hades. 20, Imri.

No 77

ACROSS: 1, Adah. 3, Watchful. 8, Pope. 9, Take care. 11, Laodiceans. 14, Energy. 15, Devise. 17, Leadership. 20, Herodias. 21, Fire. 22, Distress. 23, Eggs.

DOWN: 1, Appalled. 2, Approves. 4, Amazed. 5, Clean heart. 6, Flaw. 7, Lies. 10, Ringleader. 12, Lighting. 13, Helpless. 16, Ideals. 18, Shed. 19, Arms.

No 78

ACROSS: 1, Elated. 4, Terror. 7, Sigh. 8, Gabbatha. 9, Dictated. 13, WEF. 16, Other servants. 17, Gad. 19, Antelope. 24, Devoured. 25, Heal. 26, Stench. 27, Raised.

DOWN: 1, Easy. 2, Anguished. 3, Dogma. 4, Table. 5, Reap. 6, Ochre. 10, Tarea. 11, Theft. 12, Devil. 13, Winepress. 14, Fast. 15, Song. 18, Alert. 20, North. 21, Endor. 22, Coin. 23, Clad.

No 79

ACROSS: 1, Riddle. 4, Oracle. 8, Weary. 9, Zemirah. 10, Risen up. 11, Abner. 12, Alabaster. 17, Omega. 19, Ichabod. 21, Ahaziah. 22, Maker. 23, Detest. 24, Unshod.

DOWN: 1, Reward. 2, Dead Sea. 3, Lay on. 5, Remnant. 6, Chron. 7, Exhort. 9, Zephaniah. 13, Acacias. 14, Rebekah. 15, To hard. 16, Adored. 18, Exact. 20, Human.

No 80

ACROSS: 1, Tidy. 3, Disaster. 9, Sonship. 10, Every. 11, Eaten. 12, Is dead. 14, Deuteronomist. 17, Custom. 19, Paper. 22, Churn. 23, Nostril. 24, Telecast. 25, Send.

DOWN: 1, To steady. 2, Do not. 4, Imprisonments. 5, Ahead. 6, The Magi. 7, Rays. 8, Chance. 13, Startled. 15, Unusual. 16, Oppose. 18, Tunic. 20, Purse. 21, Scot.

★ Also from BRF ★

Seeking Faith—Finding God

Getting to grips with questions of faith

John Rackley

What does it mean to be a disciple of Jesus, living according to his Gospel today? Part of the challenge of following that path is how we communicate what we believe to friends, neighbours, colleagues and family members. But how do we explain ourselves to a society that is profoundly ignorant of God's revelation?

This book shows how our witness gains authenticity when we develop a seeking and searching faith: 'If we are to communicate what we believe, it must be as fellow travellers in these difficult and demanding times.' In five sections of reflections—A yearning faith; A gospel place; Gospel encounters; Faith companions; Praying the gospel—John Rackley wrestles with the challenge to develop such a faith and looks at what we can learn from those who first followed in Jesus' footsteps.

ISBN 978 1 84101 543 9 £6.99
Available from your local Christian bookshop or, in case of difficulty, direct from BRF using the order form on page 191.

Bridges from the Word to the World

Connecting the Bible and everyday living

Ian Coffey with Kim Bush

How can we connect our daily lives with the teaching of the Bible? How can we listen to the news and link what we hear to our faith? How should we as Christians respond to the sights and sounds that surround us every day? Bridges span—it is what they are made to do. Rivers, valleys, roadways, even stretches of the sea are crossed with ease and journeys that used to take hours are reduced to seconds. This book is called *Bridges from the Word to the World* because it is designed to span what can feel like a gap between the Bible and the rest of life.

Following on from the popular *Windows on the World from the Word* (2001) and *Doorways from the Word to the World* (2003), *Bridges* offers short reflections on a wide range of themes and happenings both national and international, linked to relevant Bible passages and short prayers to take into the day.

ISBN 978 1 84101 385 5   £7.99
Available from your local Christian bookshop or, in case of difficulty, direct from BRF using the order form on page 191.

★ Also from BRF ★

Six Men—Encountering God

Brad Lincoln

This is a book of stories—shared by six quite different men. Meet the rock climber facing a fatal fall, the wheeler-dealer whose life goes belly-up, the cynic whose prejudices are confounded, and the others who share with them a pivotal experience. Each one, in a moment of crisis or by a process of gradual realization, recognizes a God-shaped gap within. Discovering this gap and then meeting the God who fills it ends up making all the difference in the world...

Read these stories, get acquainted with the men themselves, and draw your own conclusions about the nature of the God who reveals himself in Jesus. You may feel you know this God well or you may doubt that he exists at all, but if these stories do anything, they will certainly act as a reminder that God knows us.

ISBN 978 1 84101 528 6 £6.99

Available from your local Christian bookshop or, in case of difficulty, direct from BRF using the order form on page 191.

Blind Spots in the Bible

Puzzles and paradoxes that we tend to avoid

Adrian Plass

'This book is filled with what I have called "blind spots" from the Bible. Some may be familiar passages, some more obscure, but what they have in common is at least one intriguing or disturbing aspect that I have previously missed, or noted out of the corner of my eye, but never got round to investigating or facing honestly. Why did Jesus weep at the tomb of Lazarus when he knew that his friend was about to be raised from the dead? What does the verse in Revelation mean about seeming alive when you are really dead, spiritually speaking? And what about the extraordinary bit in Genesis about angels marrying the beautiful daughters of men?

'There are, of course, many biblical stories and ideas that we will never fully understand until the day when God himself bestows the clarity that eludes us here. In the meantime, we are certainly allowed to think and analyse and question anything that strikes us as strange or inexplicable. I do hope you enjoy and benefit from my "blind spots" and I wish you a continuation of God's cheerful blessing as you investigate your own.'

ISBN 978 1 84101 505 7 £7.99

Twenty Questions Jesus Asked

What is he asking you?

Elizabeth Rundle

As Jesus tramped the Galilean and Judean countryside during the three short years of his ministry, crowds followed him. Friends and adversaries alike walked alongside him, trying to understand more of the teaching of this extraordinary person—or trap him in some way. And from time to time Jesus turned to those with him and posed questions: What do you want? Why are you so afraid? Do you believe this? Who do you say I am? To those who understood and responded to what he offered, life was never the same again.

Those same questions still hold true for all who seek to follow Jesus today. If we want to walk the way of Christ, we have to work out where we stand in relation to him. It is not a case of knowing the 'right' answer; there are no instant, easy or trite replies to the Son of God. But as we reflect on these questions for ourselves, and open ourselves to the reality of his living presence, we will be both surprised and challenged, our hearts touched and our faith deepened.

ISBN 978 1 84101 568 2 £6.99
Available (from May 2008) from your local Christian bookshop or, in case of difficulty, direct from BRF using the order form on page 191.

ORDER FORM

REF	TITLE	PRICE	QTY	TOTAL
543 9	*Seeking Faith—Finding God*	£6.99		
385 5	*Bridges from the Word to the World*	£7.99		
528 6	*Six Men—Encountering God*	£6.99		
505 7	*Blind Spots in the Bible*	£7.99		
568 2	*Twenty Questions Jesus Asked*	£6.99		

POSTAGE AND PACKING CHARGES				
Order value	UK	Europe	Surface	Air Mail
£7.00 & under	£1.25	£3.00	£3.50	£5.50
£7.01–£30.00	£2.25	£5.50	£6.50	£10.00
Over £30.00	free	prices on request		

Postage and packing:	
Donation:	
Total enclosed:	

Name ______________ Account Number ______________

Address ______________________________

______________________________ Postcode __________

Telephone Number ______________ Email ______________

Payment by: ❑ Cheque ❑ Mastercard ❑ Visa ❑ Postal Order ❑ Maestro

Card no. ☐☐☐☐ ☐☐☐☐ ☐☐☐☐ ☐☐☐☐

Expires ☐☐ ☐☐ Security code ☐☐☐ Issue no. ☐☐☐

Signature ______________________________ Date __________

All orders must be accompanied by the appropriate payment.

Please send your completed order form to:
BRF, 15 The Chambers, Vineyard, Abingdon OX14 3FE
Tel. 01865 319700 / Fax. 01865 319701 Email: enquiries@brf.org.uk

❑ Please send me further information about BRF publications.

Available from your local Christian bookshop. **BRF is a Registered Charity**